G000256433

The Quality 60

A Guide

for

Service
and
Manufacturing

by

John Bicheno

Q
60

The Gurus

The Tools

The Wastes

The New Tools

Q
60

The Techniques

The Systems

Q

60

Selecting the Right Control Chart

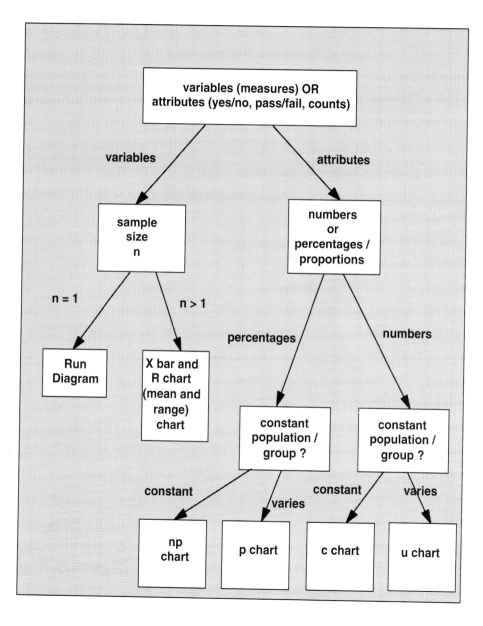

Q60 impacts with EFQM, and Service and Manufacturing

	Service	Manufacturing	Leadership	People Management	Policy and Strategy	Resources	Processes	People Satis	Customer Satisfaction	Impact on Society	Business Results
Deming	●	●	●	●	●	●	●	●	●	●	●
Juran	●	●	●	●	●	●	●	●	●	●	●
Crosby	●	●	●	●	●		●	●	●	●	●
Feigenbaum		●	●				●		●	●	●
Ishikawa	●	●	●	●		●	●	●	●		●
Garvin		●			●				●		●
Shingo		●							●		●
Taguchi		●			●	●		●		●	●
Kano	●	●			●	●		●	●		●
7 Tools	●	●					●	●	●		●
The Wastes		●					●	●		●	●
The New Tools	●	●					●	●	●		
5 S	●	●					●	●			
Benchmarking	●	●			●		●		●	●	●
Best Demonstrated Practice	●				●		●		●	●	●
Cost of Quality	●	●			●		●			●	●
c and u charts	●	●					●		●		
Cusums	●	●					●				
Cycle of Service	●			●	●				●		
Data Presentation	●	●			●		●				
Design of Experiments		●					●			●	●
Failafing (Pokayoke)	●	●					●		●	●	●
FMEA	●	●			●	●	●		●	●	●
Five Whys	●	●				●	●				
Force Field Analysis	●	●		●		●	●				
Hoshin	●	●	●	●	●	●	●		●	●	●
Importance Performance	●			●	●		●		●		
Kaizen	●	●		●	●		●	●	●	●	●
Market Survey	●	●			●				●	●	●
Moments of Truth	●	●		●					●		
Nominal Group	●	●			●	●					
Precontrol		●					●				
QFD	●	●	●		●	●	●		●	●	●
Relationships Encounters	●			●	●		●	●	●		
Service Blueprinting	●				●	●	●	●	●		
SERVQUAL	●				●		●	●	●		●
Service Recovery	●				●		●		●		●
Sixth Sigma	●			●	●		●		●		
Six Sigma	●	●					●		●		●
Supplier Partnerships	●	●			●	●	●		●		●
Yield Management	●					●	●		●		●

The 9 Gurus

Deming

Juran

Crosby

Feigenbaum

Ishikawa

Garvin

Shingo

Taguchi

Kano

The Gurus

The field of Quality Management has been strongly influenced by a number of "Gurus". Any choice of which Gurus to include would certainly include the first four given below, but beyond that opinions differ. In any case, it would be a mistake to concentrate solely on the views of one Guru. All have useful things to say. The reader has to distil out those views that are most appropriate to his or her organization.

Deming

Dr. W. Edwards Deming is probably the most revered figure in quality management. In the 1950s, Deming taught quality to the Japanese by insisting that top management attend his courses. They did, and prospered. Originally Deming taught statistical process control (SPC) to the Japanese and has always maintained that management must have an appreciation of statistical variation. Today Deming is mainly associated with quality management theories, particularly his "14 point" plan, the "Deming cycle" and his "deadly diseases". Deming died in December 1993.

Appreciation of statistical variation begins with the concept that very little in management is absolutely consistent, and that chance will account for a certain amount of "natural variation". So, for example, a salesman cannot sell exactly the same amount every month. He would have good and bad months, and the differences between good and bad are mainly explained by chance rather than by variations in the salesman's skills. Therefore merely to reward him for the good months, and to penalize for the bad could be de-motivating and poor management. On the other hand truly superior performance can produce sales which are significantly and consistently better. Here, special reward would be justified as would penalties in the case of consistently poor performance.

To illustrate the point, Deming used to do a famous experiment - the "red bead game". Five players are picked from the audience. Each is given a paddle with slots into which coloured beads fit. The players are asked to dip the paddles into a bowel containing a mix of white and red beads. The object is to get as few red beads (representing defectives) as possible. Of course, it is nearly impossible to get zero red. But the numbers of red beads varies between the players. Deming commends the player with the smallest number of reds and admonishes the player with the most reds. This is typical management behaviour according to Deming. More rounds are played, sometimes resulting in one of the players getting "fired" and others where the raise awarded to the best players "goes to his head". The audience quickly grasps the futility of paying for performance when the process is not under the player's control. The messages are that management must understand variation, and that improving the process, not motivation, is critical for success.

Common causes are inherent in the process but special causes are not, and these special causes need to be identified. Poor sales is one example but the same would apply to many other areas of both human-based and machine-based performance. (For machines, this is the basis of SPC.) Moreover, true performance improvement is very seldom within the sole power of an operator or salesman or supervisor. For example, a machine has natural variation and may be producing a certain percentage of defects. The operator can do little about it. Without management action or support significant improvement can seldom be made. Deming's rule of thumb is that perhaps 80% of improvement requires management effort, while only 20% is actionable solely by front line employees. So, mere exhortations and incentives to produce better quality will have only limited results.

It is sobering to realise that many ideas which are regarded as new and fashionable today were recommended by Deming over 30 years ago. These include continuous improvement (Kaizen) (see point 5 of the 14 points and the PDCA cycle), business process reengineering (see point 9), supplier partnership (point 4), self directed work teams (point 7), and Hoshin (point 1). Perhaps there are more ideas whose time is yet to come!

The 14 Points

Deming's 14 point plan is a complete philosophy of management, not just quality management. Books have been written on the subject. Here we attempt a brief summary.

1.   There should be a consistent message about quality, throughout the organization. It should not vary by department, by pressure of work, by time of the month, or by customer. Usually a clear statement is required from management, with actions that demonstrate that it means what is says.

2.   The new age of quality requires a commitment continuously to improve. The competition is doing this; so must you in order to survive. Customers have increasing expectations about quality.

3.   Switch from defect detection to defect prevention. Rather inspect the process than the product. Work to understand and reduce the natural variation in processes. The less the variation, the less the chance of defects.

4.   In dealing with suppliers, end the practice of awarding business on price. Move towards quality of product, reliability of delivery, and willingness to cooperate and improve. In other words build partnerships with suppliers. There should be advantages for both parties.

5.   Constantly improve. Use the PDCA cycle. (See below). Improvement is not confined to products and their direct processes, but to all supporting services and activities also.

6.   Train in a modern way. Let employees understand the concept of variation, basic SPC, improvement, and the total approach to quality. The idea is to make everyone responsible for their own quality.

7.   Supervision must change from chasing to coaching and support.

8.   "Drive out fear" of improvement. Management must create the environment which removes all possibility that improvement in quality will somehow penalize operators, through more work, loss of jobs, financial loss, or whatever.

9.   Remove any organizational barrier that prevents quality improvement. This means improved visibility between sections and also easier communications. Aim to remove any barrier that prevents the requirements and reactions of the customer being moved rapidly and without distortion to the point where action can be taken.

10. Don't have silly slogans that mean nothing. Don't have unrealistic targets. Remember, management has most of the power to make real improvements.

11. Deming's eleventh point maintains that work standards and numerical quotas should be eliminated. This is controversial, unless interpreted with the understanding of natural variation. Natural variation says that no standard or quota can be exact and without variation. If the natural variation is understood, the quotas and standards that are beyond the control of employees should not be penalized (nor rewarded for undeserved performance.)

12. Remove barriers that prevent employees having pride in their work. These barriers may include unrealistic quotas and time pressure, short-term requirements for profit rather than quality, lack of investment in the right machines or tools, individual incentive schemes based on output rather than group based schemes based on quality and improvement, and lack of management support or consistency.

13. Train and educate. This follows from point 6 but emphasises that education must be widely based and continuing. Despite being point number 13, it is usually the starting point, after point 1.

14. Create an organizational structure that will support all the previous points. This is important because the 14 point plan is not a short term implementation, but rather a long term philosophy.

The Deming Cycle (or PDCA cycle)

Deming maintains that the PDCA (Plan, Do, Check, Act) cycle is a universal improvement methodology. Deming originally called the cycle "the Shewhart cycle" after the founder of statistical quality control, but it has come to be named after Deming himself. The idea is constantly to improve so as to reduce the difference in the requirements of customers and the performance of the process.

Begin by planning what to do. This may be improvement in the design of the product and its features, or in the process which produces the product. Typically Pareto analysis is used to identify the most pressing need or problem. Then Do. This means small scale experimentation. Explore the problems, come up with possible causes, investigate them, identify the most likely ones. Then Check. Try out what you have found to see if your ideas are valid. Then Act. Implement widely if it is a success, or abandon if it is not. Where a new procedure is adopted, standardize it and make it part of the culture.

Note that the cycle is about learning, and about ongoing improvement. You learn what works and what does not in a systematic way. And the cycle repeats. After one cycle is complete, another is started.

Also note that several companies have their own version of the Deming Cycle. An example is DRIVE (Define, Review, Investigate, Verify, Execute).

THE DEMING CYCLE

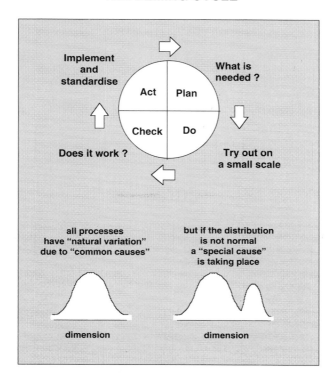

The "Deadly Diseases"
The seven "deadly diseases" of quality, as Deming terms them, amount to a severe criticism of Western management and organizational practices. The first five are closely related. They are always worth pondering, and re-pondering:

1.   "Lack of constancy of purpose" is a disease that appears in Deming's 14 point plan. It is a reminder about inconsistent policy on quality, particularly as the end-of-period rush begins! The twin of this point is;

2.   "Emphasis on short term profits" is a reminder to take a more consistent view, without being influenced by the end-of-period financial performance. And this may be brought about by the next point;

3.   Overemphasis on performance appraisal and merit rating, particularly when judged solely on financial performance. In an earlier section the issue of variation was discussed. If variation is not understood, appraisal can be literally destructive. Deming is particularly worried by the emphasis on short term results rather than on coaching and helping staff to develop their potential. This is made worse by the next two diseases;

4.   Too much staff mobility, where managers do not get to learn the real problems and requirements of an organization.

5.   Overdependence on figures, particularly financial, which can be massaged to look good in the short term, while the longer term suffers.

6 and 7. The last two points relate to excessive medical costs and excessive legal costs, which Deming believes are paralysing competitiveness. Some would regard these as being typically American problems, but they may be a foretaste of problems to come for others.

Further reading on Deming

W Edwards Deming, *Out of the Crisis*, Cambridge University Press, 1982

W Edwards Deming, *Quality, Productivity, and Competitive Position*, MIT Centre for Advanced Engineering Study, 1982

W.J. Latzko and W.J. Saunders, *Four Days with Dr Deming*, Addison Wesley, Reading, MA, 1995

Web sites

gopher://deming.eng.clemson.edu or http://deming.eng.clemson.edu

a set of Deming-related cartoons and a tour of his 14 points on http://www.cc-m.com

Juran

Like Deming, Dr. Joseph Juran is given credit for developing Japanese quality in the 1950s. His books on quality since then have had a profound influence around the world, and are so wide ranging it is difficult to highlight particular contributions from the many that have been made. Perhaps the best known Juran concepts are his definitions of quality, the concepts of "breakthrough" and the "internal customer", and the "quality trilogy". Juran also was responsible for "Pareto analysis" as applied to problem solving, for work on the costing of quality, and for the idea of a "Quality Council" within the organization. Juran has now retired from public lectures, although he continues writing. He is now in his 90's.

Juran believes quality is associated with product satisfaction and product dissatisfaction. Both require consideration. Satisfaction occurs when a product has superior performance or features. Dissatisfaction occurs when there are deficiencies or defects in the product or in its service or support. Thus there are two dimensions, an external one concerned with matching customer requirements, and an internal one concerned with building the product or service correctly. Juran has proposed the well known definition of quality as "fitness for purpose". This is not as simple as it sounds. One needs to ask, "for whose purpose", and "what is the real purpose". There may be many possible customers, both internal and external, who may use the product in different ways. (More on external customers later.) So quality begins with a close understanding of who the users will be and how and where the product will be used. Without this customer orientation, good quality is not possible.

And what is an "internal customer"? Each person along the chain, from product design to final user is both a supplier and a customer. Also, of course, the person will be a "process", carrying out some transformation or activity. The process is subject to all the concepts of process control. Taking these together, this is what Juran refers to as the "three role model", that is each stage is a supplier, a process, and customer or user. So the customer orientation mentioned earlier applies internally as well. At each stage there is opportunity to improve the product, perhaps making it easier to handle, or fit together, or maintain, or update.

Using some JURAN concepts

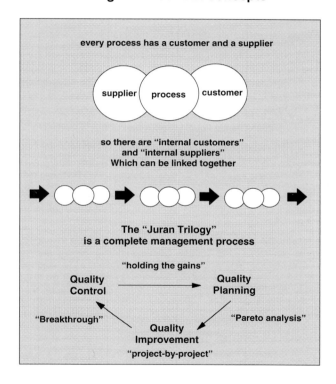

Juran emphasises the necessity for ongoing quality improvement. He maintains that this is only achieved through "project by project" improvement, in other words by a succession of small improvement projects carried out throughout the organization. Projects may be suggested by management, by operators (perhaps through quality circles) by quality specialists or by Pareto analysis of existing problems. Juran was the first to name the Pareto principle and to describe it as a universal problem solving methodology. The Pareto principle simply sets out to identify the "vital few" as opposed to the "trivial many" or the "useful many". This is the well known phenomenon that there will always be a relatively few processes or people or defects or problems that somehow take up most of the time or effort or cost. Hence it makes sense to identify these and to tackle them first. (Pareto analysis is one of the 7 tools - see that section for more detail.)

Improvement projects can also be identified through costs, and Juran was responsible for suggesting that quality costs (or the costs of not getting something right first time) should be recorded and classified. Money is the prime language of management, so that if the costs of poor quality are known this not only gets management attention but helps home in on where effort should be made. For Juran, it is necessary for middle managers in the quality area to be able to translate the language of things into the language of money and vice versa. To do this we need a classification system. Quality costs can be classified into failure costs (both internal such as scrap and rework and external such as guarantee claims and perhaps loss of custom), appraisal costs (such as inspection), and prevention costs (such as education and SPC implementation). Such costs can be obtained relatively rapidly by careful interviews or perhaps more accurately by a parallel accounting system, but in any case should be assembled in order to direct and evaluate progress on quality improvement. (For more detail see the Technique section on Cost of Quality.)

Juran emphasized that management needs to attack the "chronic" underlying poor quality that is often not even recognised. He says that there is a tendency to tackle only "sporadic" quality problems that surface from time to time. Breakthrough is needed. The way to tackle chronic quality problems is "project by project improvement". This is perhaps similar to the Deming cycle, and leads straight into the quality trilogy. The quality trilogy, according to Juran comprises quality planning, quality control, and quality improvement. These can be seen as being parallel to the financial processes of budgeting, cost control, and cost reduction. Good quality management requires the quality actions to be planned out, improved, and controlled. So the process can be seen as achieving control at one level of quality performance, then planning to be better, project by project using the tools and techniques discussed, then eventually achieving "breakthrough" to an improved level, and then once again controlling at the new level. This series of actions will not take place by chance or by a series of uncoordinated actions. Rather, they must be organized in a systematic way. This is where the "Quality Council" comes in. This body, typically comprising of senior managers, has the responsibility for coordinating the quality improvement actions and projects. They would, for example, set goals, identify needs, establish training, ensure measurements (such as costs of quality), undertake coordination, and in general liaise between quality projects and top management.

In another parallel with the Deming cycle, the Juran breakthrough sequence sees the improvement process as taking two "journeys" - the "journey from symptom to cause" and the "journey from cause to remedy". The first journey moves one from the problem to the "diagnosis" and may be seen as parallel to the "P" and "D" stages of the Deming cycle. Here we are concerned with identification, using for example Pareto, and with the generation of and testing of hypotheses as to what might be the contributing causes. The second journey moves one from the "diagnosis" to the "solution" and may be seen as parallel to the "C" and "A" stages of the Deming cycle. Here one makes the selection of the appropriate cause, implements the necessary actions, and then replicates the improvements where possible in other areas.

Juran has also written on product design. His "Road Map" has 9 junctions : identify customers, determine the needs of those customers, translate those needs into company language, develop a product that can respond to those needs, optimise the product's features to meet both company needs and customer needs, develop a process that is capable of producing the product, optimise the process, prove that the process can produce the product under operating conditions, and transfer the process to operations.

More recently, Juran has spoken about "Big Q". This is to emphasize that quality is not just the concern of production or even of total quality within the organization, but extends further into the linkage between organizations, and includes all service organizations and operations. Under Big Q the concept of "customer" extends beyond those immediately involved with producing the product or service, to include stakeholders who have a legitimate concern such as legislators and consumer groups. Juran states "In many companies there is only a dim awareness that the scope of the customer has widened, so there is no longer a consensus on who is the customer".

Finally in his last (edited) fascinating book covering the history of quality, Juran expresses his views on the future of managing for quality. He sees a parallel with the field of finance and accounting where, for example, the field is organised into distinct processes such as auditing, standard reports have been developed which are widely read and used by top managers, key terms are in widespread use, there are professional examinations, national indexes have been developed, awareness of the importance of the area will be recognized by legislators and economists, and the subject is taught in school.

Further reading on Juran

Joseph Juran, *Quality Control Handbook*, Third Edition, McGraw Hill, 1979
Joseph Juran, *Juran on Planning for Quality*, The Free Press, 1988
J.M. Juran, *Juran on Leadership for Quality*, Free Press, 1989
J.M. Juran (ed), *A History of Managing for Quality*, ASQC Quality Press, 1995
John Butman, *Juran : A Lifetime of Influence*, Wiley, New York, 1997

Web site (The Juran Institute, containing news and recent articles) :
http://www.juran.com

Crosby

Like Juran, Phil Crosby has been a prolific writer on quality. Unlike Juran, some of whose works contain much quantitative and statistical techniques, Crosby concentrates on quality philosophy, particularly relating to management. Crosby's dynamic speaking style and stimulating writing style have gained him a large following.

Crosby is perhaps best known for his "four absolutes" of quality, his phrase "quality is free", his 14 point plan (different from Deming's 14 points), and his down to earth common sense on a wide range of quality topics.

Crosby's "four absolutes" are :

1. "The definition of quality is conformance to requirements". This very specific definition of quality leaves very little open, which is probably what Crosby intends. According to Crosby, once the requirements are specified then quality is judged solely on the criteria of whether it is met or not; aesthetics or feelings don't come into it. It is then the duty of management to specify those requirements very clearly, to say what they want, and this Crosby believes is one of the major failings of management. Of course, if management does not decide what is needed then by default, operators are going to have to make that decision for the company!

2. "The system of quality is prevention". In other words, prevention is better than detection or appraisal. This is very much in line with the philosophy behind SPC; understand the process, look at what can go wrong, and take preventative actions before the process begins to deal with customers.

3. "The performance standard is zero defect", or "ZD" as Crosby calls it. Here Crosby is stating that nothing less than perfect quality has to be the aim. Setting targets below 100% is the start of a downward spiral. Of course, traditional quality management has taken zero defects to be uneconomic, and there should be a trade-off between prevention costs and failure costs. The Crosby view is now supported by a developing view that prevention costs, particularly where "total quality" is in place, do not necessarily rise massively as one approaches zero defects, but in fact rise by no more than failure costs fall. In other words, zero defect may well be optimal from a cost point of view. But again it comes back to getting the requirements right in the first place.

4.	"The measurement of quality is the price of nonconformance". Like Juran, Crosby believes in costing quality as a prime motivator for management. Crosby classifies costs into "PONC" - the price of nonconformance" (all the costs involved in not getting the product or service right) and "POC" - the price of conformance (what it costs to do things right; prevention, detection, etc.). Here Crosby's famous phrase "quality is free" is appropriate. (It is also the title of one of his books.) As he says, "it's not a gift, but it's free" or in other words if you put effort into improving quality it will more than pay for itself through improved productivity, reduced rework and claims, and improved customer satisfaction.

The problem with quality, according to Crosby, is not that people disagree with it, but what they think they know about it, namely that workers are sloppy, customers are unreasonable, close checks will find problems earlier, and that there is an economics of or trade-off in quality. In 1995 Crosby concludes that, after a brief period of improvement, these ideas are once again gaining ground.

Crosby, like Deming, has a 14 step plan for quality improvement. Deming's 14 points are more of a philosophy of quality management, whereas Crosby's are more a specific action plan for implementation. In that respect, the two 14 point plans can easily be seen as reinforcing one another. The 14 steps will not be spelled out in detail but they begin with management commitment and the establishment of a team. The next stages deal with measuring quality through "POC" and "PONC". These figures are often much higher than expected, which aids in the next steps to do with creating awareness and planning out what is to be done. Education of employees follows, with a "ZD" day to launch the program. Now employees become involved in detail goal setting as to what can be done in specific sections of the company. With the goals set, identification of the causes of defects can begin in earnest at all levels. Improvement results and recognition must then be given. Now "quality councils" allow quality managers and others to get together and review what has been achieved and how and to where else these achievements can be transferred to. This is not the end. Quality is an ongoing process, so the last step is to do it all over again.

Writing years later, Crosby now regrets putting forward his 14 point plan, making the point that many take it as a recipe for quality when what is really required is appropriate thought ("searching for specific procedures among ideas is the sign of a lazy mind"), but that such frameworks should be added to through experience, study and reflection.

Crosby's "Quality Vaccine" is perhaps more closely related to the Deming 14 point plan than the Crosby 14 step process. In typical stimulating style, Crosby's "vaccine" is preventive medicine for management against poor quality. The vaccine comprises practical advice on 21 areas, subdivided into five sections. The quality vaccine is in fact a succinct summary of what is needed for total quality management.

*	The first section deals with integrity. This is really about taking quality seriously, from chief executive to every employee. If quality is taken as "first among equals" - the others being marketing, finance, operations, and so on, then everyone understands that their own future and the future of the company will be judged on performance on quality.

*	The second section deals with systems - for quality costs, for education, for quality performance, for review and improvement, and for customer satisfaction. All of these must be designed and put in place.

*	The third section deals with the need for communication and for communication systems that will make clear the requirements and specifications, and which will communicate improvement opportunities within the organization. Crosby often emphasises the importance of listening - to customers, and to those front line employees who often know what is needed but perhaps have never been asked. Also external communications, in advertising, letters, and product information must convey a consistent message.

* The fourth section deals with operations, including working with and developing suppliers. Processes must be prepared prior to use and made capable, and process improvement must become the norm.

* And last, Crosby maintains that policies must be made clear and consistent throughout the organization.

Crosby also has a "Quality Management Maturity Grid" passing through the stages of uncertainty, awakening, enlightenment, and wisdom and certainty. During this transition the reported typical cost of quality as a percentage of sales, starts unknown, rises to 8%, then declines to 2.5%. But the actual costs of quality declines from 20% to 2.5%.

In recent years Crosby has been critical of ISO 9000 and of quality awards such as the Baldridge, saying that they are old fashioned, merely providing a living for consultants, and a recipe for managers who don't want to think about what quality really is !

Further reading on Crosby

Phil Crosby, *Quality is Free*, McGraw Hill, 1979

Phil Crosby, *Quality Without Tears*, McGraw Hill, 1984

Phil Crosby, *Let's Talk Quality*, McGraw Hill, 1989

Phil Crosby, *Quality is Still Free*, McGraw Hill, 1995

Web site

http://www.philipcrosby.com/philipcrosby/crosbymain.html

Feigenbaum

Armand Feigenbaum, an American engineer, was the originator of "Total Quality Control", now often referred to simply as total quality. In the 1950s, he defined total quality as follows :

"Total quality control is an effective system for integrating the quality development, quality maintenance, and quality improvement efforts of the various groups in an organization so as to enable production and service at the most economical levels which allow full customer satisfaction."

Feigenbaum referred to the "industrial cycle" which is the ongoing sequence of activities necessary to bring products from concept to market. Included in this cycle are marketing, design, engineering, purchasing, manufacturing, production, inspection, packaging and shipping, installation, and service. In all these stages quality has requirements to be met. Feigenbaum was the first to point out the folly of regarding quality professionals as being solely responsible for the quality function. The cycle begins and ends with the customer, but in between many people and functions must play a role; in fact everyone has a role and the responsibility must be shared. On the other hand Feigenbaum sees the quality professionals playing a central role and coordinating the entire process. He did not appear to agree with the view of quality improvement being a required role for all employees. As one moves through the cycle, there are requirements to be met at each stage, and these different requirements must be defined and communicated. This is where the quality professionals have a prime role. The total cost of quality (or non quality) accumulates through all these stages, and a total view of quality being managed through all the stages will lead to a lower overall cost.

Feigenbaum has a 40 point plan for quality which is far more detailed and specific that those of Deming or Crosby. (See the web site for a full listing). In general he has 3 steps to Quality : quality leadership, modern quality technology, and organisational commitment.

Feigenbaum is also known for his concept of the "hidden plant". That is that in every factory a certain proportion of its capacity is wasted through not getting it right first time. Feigenbaum quoted a figure of up to 40% of the capacity of the plant being wasted. At the time this was an unbelievable figure; even today some managers are still to learn that this is a figure not too far removed from the truth.

Further reading on Feigenbaum

A.V. Feigenbaum, "Total Quality Control", *Harvard Business Review*, November 1956

Armand Feigenbaum, *Total Quality Control*, (Third Edition, revised) McGraw Hill, 1991

Web sites

http://akao.larc.nasa.gov/def/key/feig40.html

http://www.asqc.org/about/history/feigen.html

Ishikawa

The late Kaoru Ishikawa is regarded as the leading Japanese contributor to quality management. His contributions are extensive but perhaps the most noteworthy are his development of the total quality viewpoint, his work on statistical quality control, his emphasis on the human side of quality, and his invention of the Ishikawa diagram and the use of the "7 tools". Perhaps most noteworthy is the fact that he is widely regarded as the "father" of quality circles, since it was he who furthered the concept of circles and popularized their practice in Japan.

Ishikawa extended the total quality view of Feigenbaum by suggesting that operators, and employees in general, have a greater role to play in all the stages suggested by Feigenbaum. In fact, Ishikawa believed that although the total quality view was invented in the West, its potential was limited there due to over-reliance on quality professionals and insufficient attention to the contribution that everyone can make. This leads directly onto quality circles and to his classification of statistical tools for quality control.

Ishikawa classified statistical quality control techniques into three groups of increasing complexity. The first group is the classic "7 tools" (which are dealt with in a complete separate section), and which require minimal statistical knowledge. (The 7 tools include the Ishikawa or fishbone diagram, which is described in that section.) Ishikawa believed that the 7 tools should be known widely, if not by everyone, in the company. They are certainly not the preserve of experts, and are simple enough for everyone to use for ongoing improvement. More specifically they should be used by quality circle members in analysing problems and devising improvements. Used together, they form a powerful set. The next group ("intermediate statistical methods"), are for use by quality specialists but also by some managers who have responsibilities for quality in their sections. Not all these managers need to know about all these methods. They include sampling surveys and sampling inspection, statistical estimation and hypothesis testing, sensory tests, and basic experimental design. These methods do require some prior knowledge of statistics but can and should be learned by relevant managers. Lastly there are some "advanced statistical methods" which are primarily for the use of specialist quality staff and consultants. These include advanced experimental design, multivariate analysis, and operations research techniques. (Note: this would include "Taguchi" methods which are discussed in a later section.)

The classification is a useful "Pareto" type of listing. First, it provides general guidance on how an educational program for quality may be set up. Second, Ishikawa believed that most quality problems - perhaps 90% or more - could be solved by the use of the 7 tools category, and that therefore they should be known to all, from company chief executive right through to operator. Ishikawa has perhaps been more instrumental than anyone in the now widely held Japanese view that without at least some knowledge of statistics, quality management is not possible. Going back to Deming's view on variation, one can notice the similarity.

Ishikawa insisted that "total quality" implies participation by everyone in the organization. Moreover, it is achieved through everyone participating in teams rather than as individuals. In this respect he talks about quality being a "thought revolution". He is critical of heavy dependence on Taylorism which he believed dehumanizes the workplace and destroys much of the opportunity for improvement. (Quality is based on "respect for humanity"). It takes time to build the necessary widespread human commitment and, according to Ishikawa, too rapid implementation of systems such as total quality and just-in-time is the reason why they have often not been a success. Quality is not a "miracle drug" but rather a "herb medicine". Despite Ishikawa's heavy inclination towards people involvement, this should not be misread as a willingness to avoid quantitative data. On the contrary, Ishikawa is adamant that collection and analysis of the hard facts and data is the essence of quality control. Hence everyone must be trained in basic tools and statistical techniques.

Ishikawa believed that quality begins with the customer. The essence is to understand customers, their requirements, what they can afford, and what their reactions are likely to be. Absolute clarity of specification is needed, and this means specifying exactly what is needed under what conditions, of for example temperature and humidity. He believed that customer complaints are a vital quality improvement opportunity, and that they must be managed. In this respect Ishikawa was the pioneer of the fashionable idea that customer complaints must be actively encouraged.

Ishikawa's quality philosophy is summarised in his 11 points which are :
1.   Quality begins and ends with education.
2 . The first step is to know customer requirements.
3.   The ideal state is when inspection is no longer necessary.
4.   Remove the root cause, not the symptoms.
5.   Quality is the responsibility of all.
6 . Do not confuse means with objectives.
7.   Put quality first to achieve long term profits.
8 . Marketing is the entrance and exit of quality.
9 . Top management should not be angered by facts shown by subordinates.
10 . 95% of problems can be solved with simple tools.
11 . Data without variability is false data.

On the perennial question of whether quality pays, Ishikawa believes that it does, provided one defines the relevant system wide enough. In other words if quality is equated with inspection then perfection may not be worthwhile. But if quality incorporates the total process, from customer to design and through process control and eventually back to the customer, then it certainly pays.

Finding the root causes of problems was important to Ishikawa, and of course his famous Ishikawa diagram assists in this respect.

As noted, Ishikawa is regarded as the "father" of quality circles. Of course he has extensive advice on how to conduct circles, but a few points are noteworthy. Primarily, circle activities must be part of a wider total quality effort. Managers must first understand both total quality and the functioning of circles before circle activities begin. Those supervisors in whose areas circles are in operation require special training. Members of a circle must be volunteers, but on the other hand everyone in a section has a role to play in quality. So it is an all or nothing affair. Circle members must be trained in appropriate tools, but must also learn to appreciate wider aspects of quality throughout the organization. The organization must cater for these requirements. A problem solving methodology must be learned by team members (Ishikawa's has 9 steps, but can be seen as similar to the Deming cycle.) Effective evaluation of circle efforts must be made. Perhaps one can summarize the Ishikawa approach with his well known axiom - that management must conduct their programs with a "belief in humanity".

Further reading on Ishikawa
Kaoru Ishikawa, *Guide to Quality Control*, Asian Productivity Association, 1976
Kaoru Ishikawa, *What is Total Quality Control? The Japanese Way*, Prentice Hall, 1985

Garvin

David Garvin, a professor at Harvard Business School, has contributed to the concept of quality as a strategy, and to our understanding of just what is meant by quality. Garvin identifies eight "dimensions" of quality, which he maintains covers the various meanings of quality that managers, operators, and customers have. The important idea is that a product or service does not usually compete on all eight, but usually targets only a select few. Likewise customers may have different perceptions as to what combination of the dimensions really add up to a "quality" package. This implies that management must seek to understand customer perceptions, so that quality efforts will be focused. Also there may be opportunities to compete on different or additional dimensions that are not offered by competitors. The eight dimensions are:

1. **Performance**, which is the primary operating characteristics of the product or service. Examples would be size, speed, power, sound.

2. **Features**, which are the "extras" that supplement the main performance characteristics. The "sunroof and spotlamps".

3. **Reliability**. What may go wrong and how often it is likely to.

4. **Conformance** which is the closeness of match between the design specification and what is actually produced (or the match between what is advertised and what is experienced by customers).

5. **Durability** which is to do with how long the product may last, and its robustness in operating conditions. How often service is needed is also relevant.

6. **Serviceability** which is to do with the ease, speed, cost and friendliness of service. Whereas reliability is concerned with mean time between failures (MTBF), serviceability is concerned with mean time to repair (MTTR).

7. **Aesthetics**. The appearance, style, "class" and impression.

8. **Perceived Quality**. The "feel", the "finish", and perhaps the reputation. Also the friendliness and the manner in which the customer is served.

Not all dimensions are applicable in the service sector and often other dimensions may be added or substituted. These could include friendliness, helpfulness, clarity of communication, knowledge, safety and security, decision making ability, and response time.

The dimensions are useful because they help understand the breadth of the challenge which is involved in managing quality. In marketing, there is the well known "marketing mix", the point being that product, price, place, and promotion need to be made compatible as a single package. There is apparently also a "quality mix" which requires the same degree of care in its formulation.

Further reading on Garvin
David Garvin, "Managing Quality", The Free Press, 1988

Shingo (and Failsafing)

The late Shigeo Shingo is strongly associated with Just-in-Time manufacturing and may not be classified as a quality guru by all. Nevertheless his work on so-called "pokayoke" or fail-safe devices is very significant and is already widely implemented. For this reason he is bound to be considered as one of the "greats" sooner or later.

The late Shigeo Shingo did not invent failsafing ("pokayoke" in Japanese, literally mistake proofing), but developed and classified the concept, particularly in manufacturing. More recently failsafing in services has developed. Shingo's book *Zero Quality Control : Source Inspection and the Pokayoke System* is the classic work.

A failsafing device is a simple, often inexpensive, device which literally prevents defects from being made. The characteristics of a failsafing device are that it undertakes 100% automatic inspection (a true pokayoke would not rely on human memory or action), and either stops or gives warning when a defect is discovered. Note that a pokayoke is not a control device like a thermostat or toilet control valve that takes action every time, but rather a device that senses abnormalities and takes action only when an abnormality is identified.

Shingo distinguishes between "mistakes" (which are inevitable) and "defects" (which result when a mistake reaches a customer.). The aim of pokayoke is to design devices which prevent mistakes becoming defects. Shingo also saw quality control as a hierarchy of effectiveness from "judgment inspection" (where inspectors inspect), to "informative inspection" where information is used to control the process as in SPC, and finally to "source inspection" which aims at checking operating conditions "before the fact". Good pokayokes fall into this last category.

POKAYOKE in SERVICE

	Control	Warning
Contact	Parking height bars Armrests on seats	Staff mirrors Shop entrance bell
Fixed Value	French fry scoop Pre-dosed medication	Trays with indentations
Motion Step	Airline lavatory doors	Spellcheckers Beepers on ATMs

after: Failsafe Services :
Richard Chase and Douglas Stewart, OMA Conference, 1993

According to Shingo there are thee types of failsafing device: "contact", "fixed value", and "motion step". This means that there are six categories, as shown in the figure with service examples.

The contact type makes contact with every product or has a physical shape which inhibits mistakes. An example is a fixed diameter hole through which all products must fall; an oversize product does not fall through and a defect is registered. The fixed value method is a design which makes it clear when a part is missing or not used. An example is an "egg tray" used for the supply of parts. Sometimes this type can be combined with the contact type, where parts not only have to be present in the egg tray but also are automatically correctly aligned. The motion step type automatically ensures that the correct number of steps have been taken. For example, an operator is required to step on a pressure-sensitive pad during every assembly cycle, or a medicine bottle has a press-down-and-turn feature for safety. Other examples are a checklist, or a correct sequence for switches which do not work unless the order is correct.

Shingo further developed failsafe classification by saying that there are five areas that have potential for failsafing : the operator (Me), the Material, the Machine, the Method, and the Information (4 M plus I). An alternative is the process control model comprising input, process, output, feedback, and result. All are candidates for failsafing. According to Grout, areas where pokayoke should be considered include areas where worker vigilance is required, where mispositioning is likely, where SPC is difficult, where external failure costs dramatically exceed internal failure costs, and in mixed model and JIT production.

Shingo says that pokayoke should be thought of as having both a short action cycle (where immediate shut down or warning is given), and also a long action cycle where the reasons for the defect occurring in the first place are investigated. John Grout makes the useful point that one drawback of pokayoke devices is that potentially valuable information about process variance may be lost, thereby inhibiting improvement.

In an extension of Shingo's work, Richard Chase of University of Southern California has extended Shingo's work to Services. He discusses stages of failsafing by both the provider and the customer. The service provider's work should attempt to be failsafed at the task stage (doing the actual work), at the treatment stage (the interaction with the customer - for instance customer greeting), and with the tangibles (the physical appearance, cleanliness etc). On the Customer side, failsafing could be attempted at three stages, equivalent to Vandermerwe's Pre, During, and Post stages of customer service.

A systematic way to consider failsafing is to construct a Cycle of Service diagram (see separate section), and then for each Moment of Truth consider how it may be failsafed.

Further reading
Shigeo Shingo, *Zero Quality Control : Source Inspection and the Pokayoke System,* Productivity Press, 1986
Richard Chase and Douglas Stewart, "Make Your Service Fail Safe", *Sloan Management Review,* Spring 1994, pages 35-44

Web site on Shingo
The Shingo prize for JIT and Quality. Details at
http://www.phoenixcg.com/shingo/html

An impressive site with numerous examples and pictures is at :
http://www.cox.smu.edu/jgrout/poke-yoke.html

An example of pokayoke in software engineering is at :
http://www.cox.smu.edu/jgrout/pokasoft.html

http://akao.larc.nasa.gov/dfc/pokyok.html

and Shingo philosophy on
http://www.dmu.ac.uk/dept/schools/business/corporate/tqmex/shingo.ht

Taguchi

Genichi Taguchi is a Japanese statistician and engineer whose concepts only began to make an impact in the West during the 1980s. His principal contributions have been to our understanding of what product specification really means for quality and how such specifications can be translated into cost effective production. Quality through design could be a short summary.

Taguchi has been critical of the conventional view of quality acceptance, which is that there are specification limits within which a product is acceptable and beyond which it not. This back-and-white or perfect and defective is not the way most customers see quality, nor is it effective in a design or engineering sense, argues Taguchi. For instance, a meal served in a restaurant is not suddenly defective on one side of a particular temperature and perfect on the other. Nor are part dimensions which when changed by a fraction of a millimetre suddenly become defective. Taguchi argues instead for a continuous decline in utility as one moves further away from the target or optimal value. Taguchi refers to this as the "loss function". The function is called this because, Taguchi maintains, any deviation involves a "loss to society" over the lifetime of the product. He maintains that the loss is approximately proportional to the square of the deviation from the target value. That is, as the distance away from the target value doubles, the "loss" will increase by four times. Another interesting view is that there are "customer tolerance limits" rather than engineering or designer specified limits. So although there may be no sharp cutoff of acceptability as far as the design specification is concerned, there will eventually be limits beyond which a customer finds the product or service unacceptable.

Acceptance of the loss function has an important implication for quality improvement. Instead of crossing the limit to achieve acceptance and then ceasing further improvement effort, the loss function would suggest that improvement must be ongoing until the target perfection is achieved. Specification limits become superfluous. This ultimate goal is virtually impossible (there will always be a new magnitude of accuracy to challenge) so the improvement effort must never cease. Perhaps this would explain the apparent Japanese devotion to improvement (in Japan the Taguchi view is more well established) in contrast to more relaxed behaviour elsewhere.

Taguchi believes that it is preferable to design a product which is robust or insensitive to variation in the manufacturing process than it is to attempt to control all the many variations during actual manufacture. Instead of taking measures to control factors which degrade the performance of a product ("noise"), he believes in reducing their influence. Taguchi is fond of quoting an example from tile making where, instead of trying to control all the factors, such as temperature and pressure, and human error, which have an influence on tile dimensions, by altering the tile mix the process becomes much more robust to changes in these factors.

Like many great ideas, this is beautifully obvious. The trick is to put it into practice. This is where Taguchi's ideas on parameter design and the control of experiments come in. Experimental design is a well established body of knowledge in the field of statistics and was not invented by Taguchi. But Taguchi has made these concepts more usable and practical for the quality professional. In traditional statistical analysis, often scores of experiments have to be carried out to identify the sensitive parameters. This often puts their practical use out of bounds, but with Taguchi's methods the amount of work is drastically reduced. The object of the experiments is to identify the design parameter settings that minimise the effect of "noise", by systematically varying the design parameters and the noise factors and observing the outcome. Whilst it is true that Taguchi methods are probably beyond the statistical abilities of most operators, they can be appreciated by managers and used by designers. With the Taguchi view, design is the principal determinant to the final product cost, over its lifetime.

A distinction is therefore made between "off line" quality control, which include sensitivity tests and reliability tests, and "on line" quality control which are concerned with control during manufacture.

As Taguchi sees it, product development has three stages. The first, "system design", is a non statistical stage which brings together engineering and marketing/customer knowledge to produce a prototype design. In the second, "parameter design", the relationship of desirable product performance to changing parameters is explored. This amounts to finding a robust design, in other words the most cost effective way in which performance can remain good irrespective (within limits) to changes in operating conditions. The "secret" of this is to use the non-linear effects of product parameters on performance characteristics. (Refer to the tile example). The third stage is "tolerance design" which now sets tolerances around the target

Some TAGUCHI concepts

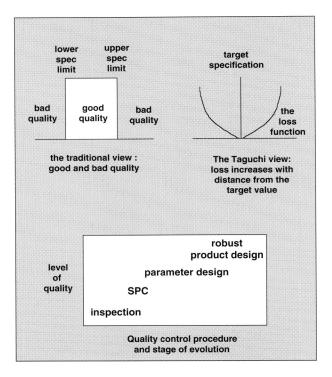

settings, not by the usual engineering techniques relating to "tolerance stackup", but by finding the right trade-off between society loss and manufacturing cost. All this sounds terribly complex. It is not, but it is also not simple. There are now thousands of successful examples.

Today several companies see a close link between Taguchi methods and quality function deployment, which is discussed in the technique section.

We can view Taguchi methods along a continuum, being that inspecting the process (SPC) is superior to inspecting the product (SQC). And reducing the sensitivity of parameters is an advance on SPC because the process does not have to be so tightly controlled. And best of all is robust design where product performance remains good in spite of changes in operating characteristics.

Further reading on Taguchi
Genichi Taguchi, *System of Experimental Design*, UNIPUB Kraus, 1985
Glen Stuart Peace, *Taguchi Methods : A Hands-On Approach*, Addison Wesley, 1993

Kano

Dr. Noriaki Kano is a Japanese academic who is best known for his excellent "Kano model". The Kano Model has emerged as one the most useful and powerful aids to product and service design and improvement available.

The Kano model relates three factors (which Kano argues are present in every product or service) to their degree of implementation or level of implementation, as shown in the diagram. Kano's three factors are Basic (or "must be") factors, Performance (or "more is better") factors, and Delighter (or "excitement") factors. The degree of customer satisfaction ranges from "disgust", through neutrality, to "delight".

THE KANO MODEL

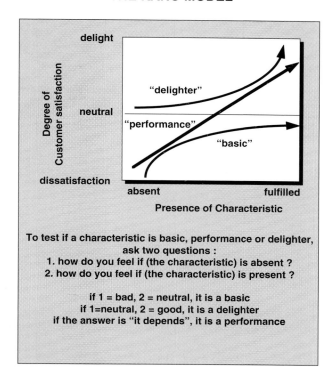

To test if a characteristic is basic, performance or delighter, ask two questions :
1. how do you feel if (the characteristic) is absent ?
2. how do you feel if (the characteristic) is present ?

if 1 = bad, 2 = neutral, it is a basic
if 1=neutral, 2 = good, it is a delighter
if the answer is "it depends", it is a performance

A Basic factor is something that a customer simply expects to be there. If it is not present the customer will be dissatisfied or disgusted, but if it is fully implemented or present it will merely result in a feeling of neutrality. Examples are clean sheets in a hotel, a station tuner on a radio, or windscreen washers on a car. Notice that there may be degrees of implementation: sheets may be clean but blemished. Basic factors should not be taken for granted, or regarded as easy to satisfy; some may even be exceptionally difficult to identify. One example is course handouts which a lecturer may regard as trivial but the audience may regard as a basic necessity. If you don't get the basics right, all else may fail - in this respect it is like Maslow's Hierarchy of Needs : it is no good thinking about self esteem needs unless survival needs are catered for. Market research is of limited value for basics (because they are simply expected). Therefore a designer needs to build up a list by experience, observation and organised feedback.

A Performance factor can cause disgust at one extreme, but if fully implemented can result in delight. This factor is also termed "more is better" but could also be "faster is better" or "easier is better". Performance factors are usually in existence already, but are neutral, causing neither disgust nor delight. It is not so much the fact that the feature exists, it is how it can be improved. The challenge to identify them, and to change their performance. Examples are speed of check in at a hotel, ease of tuning on a radio, or fuel consumption. Performance factors represent real opportunity to designers and to R&D staff. They may be identified through market research, but observation is also important, especially to identify performance features that are causing dissatisfaction. Creativity or process redesign is often required to deliver the factor faster or easier, and information support may play a role as in the "one minute" check-in at some top hotels. The Cycle of Service (see separate section) is a useful starting point to identify performance factors.

Finally, A Delighter is something that customers do not expect, but if present may cause increasing delight. Examples are flowers and wine awaiting guest arrivals in some hotel rooms, or a radio tuner that retunes itself when moving out of range of a transmitter. By definition, market research is of little use here. Once again, it is creativity, based on an appreciation of (latent) customer needs that can provide the breakthrough. But we need to be careful about Delighters also : a true Delighter is provided at minimal extra cost - it would certainly cause customer delight to give them all a complimentary car, but would be disastrous for company finances. Therefore, perhaps a more appropriate hotel Delighter would be to give guests a choice of sheet colour, pillow type (English or German), and sheet type (linen, satin, or wool).

We should also note that the Kano factors are not static. What may be a Delighter this year may migrate towards being a Basic in a few years time. And also, what may be a Delighter in one part of the world may be a Basic in another. Thus it is crucial to keep up to date with changing customer expectations. Benchmarking may be a way to go. From Kano we also learn that a reactive quality policy, reacting to complaints, or dissatisfiers, will at best lead to neutrality but proactive action is required to create delight.

The Kano Model works well with Quality Function Deployment. Basics should be satisfied, and delighters can be explicitly traded off in the "roof" of the QFD matrix (for example fuel consumption may suggest a lighter car, but safety suggests a stronger one - so the quest is to find material that is light, strong, and inexpensive.)

Further reading:
Unfortunately readings in English are difficult to obtain, but an excellent article is Hofmeister, Walters, Gongos, "Discovering Customer WOW's", *Annual Quality Congress*, ASQC, May 1996, pp759-770.

Joiner, B.L., *Fourth Generation Management*, McGraw Hill, New York, 1994

Lou Cohen, *Quality Function Deployment*, Addison Wesley, Reading MA, 1995, pp 36-41

The 7 Tools

Process Chart
Pareto Analysis
Ishikawa Diagram
Histogram and Measles Chart
Run Diagram and Correlation
Process Control Charts
Check Sheets

Q
60

The "7 Tools" of Quality

The seven tools of quality were originally assembled by Kaoru Ishikawa for use with quality circles. The seven tools, when used together or even individually, are a "first line" attacking force for quality improvement. They are taught to a large proportion of operators in Japan and are now increasingly used by operators worldwide. Many people in the service industry will find them equally useful. The tools themselves are basically a simple and long established set of techniques for data analysis in a work situation. The most recent of the tools is the Ishikawa or fishbone diagram, which Dr. Ishikawa developed to assist in quality circle "brainstorming". The tools are presented below in the order in which they are commonly used, although many variations are possible.

Web site

A general web site with reference material on many tools and techniques is at
http://mijuno.larc.nasa.gov/dfc/qtec.html

The Process Chart

The process chart lists every step that is involved in the manufacture of a product or the delivery of a service. It has long been used by work study officers, who usually use special symbols to indicate "operation", "delay", "move", "store", and "inspect". (See figure). The process chart helps identify waste, (or MUDA) and documents the process completely. Good communication is an important reason to do this. The systematic record helps reveal the possible sources of quality and productivity problems. Three important variations of the process chart are the flowchart, the service blueprint and the "cycle of service" (see separate sections).

It is a good idea to draw the process chart using the standard symbols because this aids clarity. The chart can be plotted against a time scale if time if critical. Process charts should also be used to document a process after it has been changed. This serves as a future record and can be used for "auditing" the process - to see if it is still being carried out in the way it was designed.

Many companies already have process charts. If they are available, beware! There are often differences between the "official" process charts and the way things actually happen in practice. The team or analyst should take the time to follow through a number of products, services or customers, documenting any "horror stories" that occur. Often several actions and "rework loops", unknown to management will be discovered. But it is not the purpose of the chart to use it for "policing". Often a team will draw up a chart for their own use in improvement and should not be obliged to turn it over to management.

Some process charts can be very long and complicated. If so, break them up into sections of responsibility. Also use a hierarchy, with the overall process shown in outline and the detail on several sub-charts.

In the service sector process charts can be made more effective by dividing the page into two halves. On the one half is shown those actions where there is direct interaction with external customers. On the other half is shown actions that are entirely internal. So, for example, in the process chart of checking a guest out of a hotel, the front desk sequence of actions are shown on the left and the accounts office actions on the right. The two halves are, of course, linked by the complete sequence of events.

A flowchart is similar to a process chart and is often used when there are decisions involved. The symbol for a decision, a diamond, would lead to branching as a result of different decisions. Flowcharts are often used with computer systems and usually do not include the standard process chart symbols. However there is no reason why these symbols should not be combined.

In the service industry a well known version of the process chart or flowchart is the "cycle of service" named by Albrecht and Zemke in their book "Service America!". Usually a cycle of service is drawn as a circle with the events written in at points on the circumference. The essential difference is that a cycle of service is the sequence of events that a customer experiences in dealing with the organization. Each event is a potential "moment of truth" that a customer may experience. (See the section on this technique.) So a process chart often documents the events experienced by a product or document in its progress through the factory or office, but the cycle of service follows a customer. Of course, customers interact but products do not. Also products and documents can be delayed and stored but this is not possible or desirable with customers! As a result managers interpret the diagrams differently, looking out for waste in the process chart but points of potential dissatisfaction in the case of cycles of service.

Whether using a process chart, a flowchart, or a cycle of service, these charts are best assembled using a team approach, preferably the people who are "front line". Using the charts the team can begin systematically to document the nature of quality problems and defects. This leads onto the next tool.

The PROCESS CHART and FLOWCHART

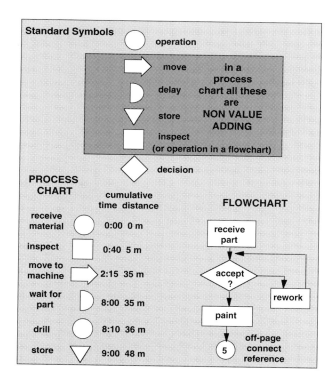

Note : There is actually a family of process charts that is used by work study officers and industrial engineers. These are less frequently used by other staff, but they may be useful, particularly for productivity improvement. For instance, the "person-machine" process chart lists, against a time scale, what the person is doing side by side with what the machines that he/she is operating are doing. This enables wasteful time gaps to be identified. Details on these more specialized charts can be found in textbooks on Method Study.

Further reading

Karl Albrect and Ron Zemke, *Service America!*, Dow Jones-Irwin, 1985
Karl Albrect and Lawrence Bradford, *The Service Advantage*, Richard D Irwin, 1990
Dianne Galloway, *Mapping Work Processes*, ASQC Quality Press, Milwaukee, WI, 1994

Pareto Analysis.

Pareto analysis goes under several names. Alternative names are ABC analysis and the "80/20" rule. Whatever the name, it is one of the most effective yet simple tools available. Pareto analysis gives recognition to the fact that, invariably, a small number of problem types account for a large percentage of the total number of problems that occur. The name "80/20" is representative of this; perhaps 80% of all problems are due to 20% of all the types of problem that occur. (Often 90/10 would be more typical.) The name ABC is also a good one. This suggests that the range of types of problem be classified into A, B, and C categories, designating their importance.

(Pareto analysis is also good practice in many other fields of management; for instance inventory control, forecasting, marketing, and personnel.)

It makes good sense to tackle the most pressing problems first; the "vital few" as Juran calls them. When these are successfully eliminated or reduced, of course, another problem will head the list. So now tackle that one. And so on. Continuing in this way is an effective ongoing improvement methodology.

Pareto analysis begins by ranking problems from highest to lowest. See the example. Then the cumulative number of problems is plotted on the vertical axis of the graph. Along the horizontal axis are arranged the problems in descending order. It can be seen that the resulting graph rises rapidly then tails off to an almost flat plateau. Now it is easy to pick out how many problems need top priority attention.

Now the team has used the process chart to list and classify the problems, and Pareto analysis to identify the most serious problems. In the next stage the team would begin to explore possible causes and their solution.

The Ishikawa Diagram

The Ishikawa diagram, also known as the "Cause and Effect" diagram and the "fishbone" diagram, is used to brainstorm out possible contributing causes of a particular problem or defect. In this respect it follows directly from the Pareto diagram, with the most pressing problem becoming the spine of the "fish". An example is shown in the figure. The name of "fishbone" is clearly representative of the form.

As can be seen, contributing causes are written in on the diagram, arranged in a hierarchy. Hence the name "cause and effect". If some difficulty is experienced in starting off the diagram, use the "4 M's" (men/people, machines, methods, materials) as four initial "bones". Other alternatives for service operations are to use the "4 P's" (Places, Procedures, People, Policies), or the "4 S's" (Surroundings, Suppliers, Systems, Skills). Usually the diagram is built with one person writing in points on the diagram and a team contributing their ideas.

The beauty of the Ishikawa diagram is the concise and visual way in which contributing causes can be documented on one diagram. It requires literally seconds of instruction in order for any employee to understand.

The 7 TOOLS : Pareto and Fishbone

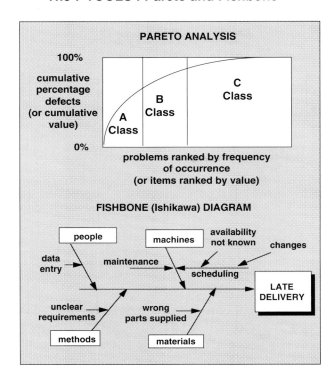

A variation on the Ishikawa diagram is the "CEDAC" diagram, originally developed by Fakuda. CEDAC stands for "cause and effect diagram with addition of cards". It is the same Ishikawa diagram except that cards, containing notes and ideas on each particular cause, are added to the diagram. Usually there are slots made for each cause, giving access to a pocket into which cards are placed. This addition is very useful because it allows elaboration on the thinking. The diagram can be kept on display, and as further information or thoughts are acquired, they are added to the pockets. This prevents "reinventing the wheel". Fakuda has developed the CEDAC concept into a complete improvement methodology.

Now with the range of possible causes identified, it seems a good idea to firm up on the information that is available. This is where the next tool comes in.

Further reading
*   Ryuji Fakuda, *Managerial Engineering*, Productivity Press, 1983

The Histogram and Measles Chart

The histogram has much in common with the Pareto diagram. It is used to show graphically the relative number of occurrences of a range of events. Using vertical bars, it plots frequency on the vertical axis against events, arranged one after the other on the horizontal axis. (See the figure.)

Following from the Ishikawa diagram, data is collected and classified according to each of the causes suggested. This data is shown on a histogram, from which the most important causes should be apparent. As with the Pareto diagram, it is then clear which are the causes that require further investigation.

The 7 TOOLS : Histogram and Measles Chart

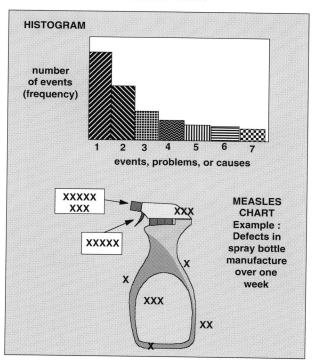

HISTOGRAM

number of events (frequency)

1 2 3 4 5 6 7

events, problems, or causes

MEASLES CHART
Example :
Defects in spray bottle manufacture over one week

Histograms can be used to collect data literally as it happens. Here a flip chart is set up right at the workstation. As problems occur they are written down on the flipchart. When the same problem recurs, a tick is placed next to that problem. In effect this is building up a histogram. (In this case the histogram is lying on its side, but that does not matter.) The problems with the most ticks are obviously the most frequently occurring and most urgent problems. Such a flipchart histogram has the great advantages of being easy to use, visible for all, and up to date.

A special form of histogram, with similarities to the flip chart procedure, is the Measles chart. Here defects or problems are simply plotted on an engineering drawing, blueprint or map at the location where the problem occurs. The accumulation of marks on the drawing gives an excellent impression as to where the problems lie. It avoids numerical or written description and may lead to the rapid identification of related problems. (A symmetry of the defects may indicate a process problem, but a lack of symmetry may indicate a maintenance or wear problem.) Of course, there are extensions of this technique - times can be written in, or different symbols used for different operators.

The histogram helps identify likely causes. Now the next stage requires some experimentation to find out how that cause can be eliminated. The next set of tools is appropriate.

Run Diagrams, Correlation Diagrams and Stratification

Run diagrams and correlation diagrams are used to explore relationships between events and time, and between problems and causes. They are used for basic experimentation, to find out when and how problems arise and how problems can be rectified. Despite sounding rather scientific, they are often simple but very effective, and certainly within the capability of most operators and front line personnel.

The 7 TOOLS : Run Diagram

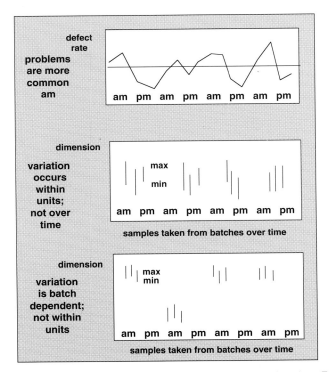

The run diagram is simply a graph of the number of events plotted against time. For instance, a record can be kept of the number of complaints over time. This may reveal that complaints occur at the beginning of the month or at a certain time of day. If defects produced on a machine are plotted against time, one may discover that most defects tend to occur when the machine has been used for some time (hot?) or just after the tea-break (carelessness?). A common use for a run chart is to detect slow trends (i.e. a gradual increase or decrease). For this, the charts have to be maintained over a long period.

The correlation diagram is used for more specific experimentation. Usually defect level (or some other measure of performance) is plotted on the vertical axis and the "experimental variable" on the horizontal. An example would be rejects against temperature. (Perhaps as temperature rises rejects fall, but then around a specific temperature rejects begin to increase again.) This could either be found out by a specific experiment involving deliberately varying the temperature, or by simply counting rejects and taking the temperature from time to time in the normal course of operation.

The 7 TOOLS : Correlation and Stratification

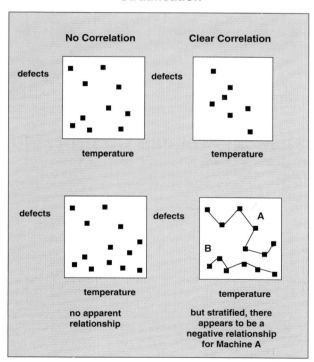

Very often no relationship (or "correlation") is found. So something else has to be tried. Perhaps first temperature, then pressure, then temperature divided by pressure, and so on. (In services, perhaps customer wait time against number of servers, or customer response time against quantity of information displayed on a screen.) Eventually, and with intelligent guesswork, good relationships can be found. This detective work can be a lot of fun, and front line people are often good at it because they have an appreciation of the real factors that make a difference. Normally an attempt is made to hold other factors as constant as possible while one factor at a time is varied.

There is a measure of correlation, called the "correlation coefficient", which can be calculated by formula. This measure is to be found "built in" on many scientific calculators, but is not given here. The reason why it is not given is that it is always preferable to plot the results on graph paper and to judge the relationship visually. Only in more extensive experiments (such as the Taguchi methods) is detailed calculation necessary.

Often both run diagrams and correlation diagrams will be used. First a run diagram is used for more general analysis and to see if time of day or month has an effect. Then follows a correlation study for the specifics. There are other possibilities as well. A common one is the matrix, where, for example, errors are recorded in a matrix which shows operator names along one axis and types of error or time of day along the other axis. This would reveal, perhaps, that different operators are good at different things or have different error-prone periods.

Stratification simply means splitting the data into groups and plotting the results on graphs. For instance, defect data against time may appear to have no particular pattern, but when data for individual operators or machines is plotted the situation may suddenly clarify. Clearly there is often a large number of ways in which data can be separated out; by operator, machine, material, time, batch, product, customer, location are just a few. But once a team knows about stratification they are likely to make good suggestions as to how it can be separated. Of course, this means that care has to be taken in the first place as to how the data is collected. It is a learning process.

Run diagrams, correlation diagrams and stratification have the effect of identifying what are termed "special causes". These are the events or defects which cannot be explained by natural variation of the process. (More on this later.) So having identified and solved some of these problems, it may now be time to set up a more sophisticated control mechanism to bring the process under control and to keep it under control. This is the next tool, and a major one.

Statistical Process Control (SPC)

Statistical process control (SPC) aims at achieving good quality during manufacture through prevention rather than detection. It is concerned with controlling the process (or machine) which makes the product. If the process is good, then the products will automatically be good. So the process or machine which makes the product is inspected rather than inspecting the product itself. This is really proactive management - inspecting and controlling the process before the event, rather than reactive management - inspecting the product after the event.

SPC is not of course the full answer to total quality. A poorly designed product can conform to all manufacturing requirements, but still fail to convince customers that it is a quality product. So SPC is just one of the tools in the toolkit - albeit a major tool.

Perhaps confusingly at first, the best way to find out what is happening to a process is to take measurements of the products that the process is producing. Of course you do not need to look at every product that is produced. Instead you take samples, and use statistics to judge what is happening to the process. This is why it is called statistical process control. It may seem as if one is inspecting a few of the products coming out of the process, but in fact it is the process that is being inspected and controlled.

SPC is undertaken through the use of charts on which the performance of the process is plotted. If the process starts to go haywire it can be stopped in good time before many or any defectives are made. We begin by examining the types and content of these SPC charts.

Types of chart : variables and attributes
There are two main types of chart - variables and attributes. A variables chart measures some characteristic that is variable along a scale, such as length or the number of scratches. It is something that can be measured. An attribute chart is used where there only two possibilities - pass or fail, yes or no. With an attribute, a judgement is made rather than a measurement taken.

Variables charts : The average and range chart

The main variables chart is the "average and range" chart, also known as the "x bar and r chart". This is actually two charts, one which tracks the average measurement of the sample taken, and the other the range of the sample, that is the maximum minus the minimum value. Both are necessary. For instance the average of a sample of five may be fine, but the range could be unacceptably wide. And the range could be small, but located in the wrong place; that is it has an undesirable average. So typically, from time to time throughout the day, the operator will take, say, the five most recent products produced and set them aside. This is a "sample". The particular product dimension is measured and the average and range values of the sample calculated. These two results are plotted on the chart, usually by the process operator. The chart indicates if the process is acceptable. If it is acceptable work continues. If not, work stops to investigate. That is SPC in practice.

STATISTICAL PROCESS CONTROL (SPC)

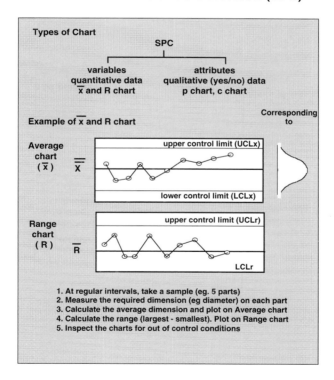

Types of Chart

SPC

variables
quantitative data
x̄ and R chart

attributes
qualitative (yes/no) data
p chart, c chart

Corresponding
to

Example of x̄ and R chart

Average
chart
(x̄)   x̿   upper control limit (UCLx)

lower control limit (LCLx)

Range
chart
(R)   R̄   upper control limit (UCLr)

LCLr

1. At regular intervals, take a sample (eg. 5 parts)
2. Measure the required dimension (eg diameter) on each part
3. Calculate the average dimension and plot on Average chart
4. Calculate the range (largest - smallest). Plot on Range chart
5. Inspect the charts for out of control conditions

Refer to the figure. Notice that both the average and the range charts have an upper and a lower "control limit". These limits are the bounds beyond which unacceptable performance is indicated.

Natural variation of the process

This brings us to the concept of "natural variation". (This was also discussed under the section on Dr. Deming.) Every process has natural variation. In other words, it is impossible to make any product with absolute consistency. The inconsistency will be caused by chance variations, however small, in, perhaps, the material, tool wear, positioning of the piece, speed of the machine, actions by the operator, and so on. These are called common causes. This variation can be measured and, using statistics, its spread can be predicted. It turns out that the spread follows a particular pattern, known as the normal distribution, irrespective of the type of process, so long as samples are being taken, and there are not "special events" taking place. The special events are assignable to unusual or unexpected changes or events, which may cause defects to be produced. This knowledge is very convenient for two reasons.

First, if the variation does not follow a normal distribution then we know that some special event is taking place. The special event may be an untrained operator, a change in the type of material, tool or bearing wear-out and so on. These special events can, with perseverance, be tracked down and the cause eliminated.

SPC FORMULAS

x and R charts

Assume samples of size 3 are taken
the readings are x1, x2, x3

$$\overline{x} = \frac{x1 + x2 + x3}{3} \qquad R = \text{largest } x - \text{smallest } x$$

these are the two values that are plotted on the charts

To set up the chart, take 20 (minimum) random samples,
each of sample size (say) 3
Calculate x and R as above, then

$$\overline{\overline{x}} = \frac{\overline{x}1 + \overline{x}2 + \overline{x}3 + \ldots\ldots + \overline{x}20}{20} \qquad \overline{R} = \frac{R1 + R2 + \ldots\ldots + R20}{20}$$

These give the average (x and R) lines on the chart
Then calculate the control limits using the formulas
$UCLx = \overline{\overline{x}} + A2 * \overline{R}$ $UCLr = D4 * \overline{R}$
$LCLx = \overline{\overline{x}} - A2 * \overline{R}$ $LCLr = D3 * \overline{R}$

where the values A2, D3, D4 depend on the sample size

sample size	A2	D3	D4
3	1.023	0	2.575
4	0.729	0	2.282
5	0.577	0	2.115
6	0.483	0	2.004
7	0.419	0.076	1.924

Second, the spread of a normal distribution can be measured by calculating the control limits. The formula is given in the figure. It turns out that within these limits (which equal plus or minus three "standard deviations" on either side of the process average value), lies virtually all of the natural variation. So if an operator takes a measurement and finds that it lies outside these control limits, then it is virtually certain that something has happened to the process. The process is then referred to as being "out of control". The process should be stopped and the situation investigated.

Setting up the control chart

Charts must be set up for each process - that is for each machine, making a particular type of product. (Pre-printed SPC charts are available from some Quality societies or in books, and these make data entry and chart plotting very easy.) When setting up a chart it is important that there is consistency, so samples should be taken over a representative period of time. You will need to decide on a sample size and the number of samples. Typical numbers are a sample size of 5 and at least 20 samples. For each sample calculate the average ("mean") and the range. Refer to the figure. Then calculate the average of the averages, and the average of the ranges. Now you will need to look up the control limit factors for the sample size you have used. (If you have used a sample size of 5, the factors are given in the figure.). Now use the formulas in the figure to calculate the control limits. When these are drawn in you can begin to use the charts for control purposes. You will have to decide what is a reasonable interval for samples to be taken. Generally, the higher the "Cpk" value, the less frequent does the sampling have to be. (See the section which follows on capability.)

Chart interpretation

There are other criteria, apart from falling outside of the control limits, that indicate an out of control situation. These other criteria can also be identified by operators, so that early action can be taken.

STATISTICAL PROCESS CONTROL
Tracing Problems through Charts

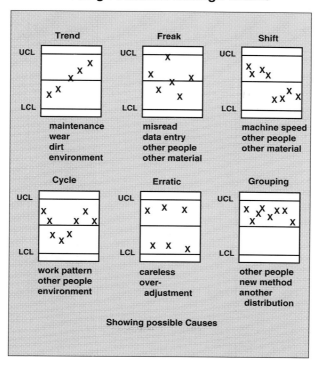

With natural variation occurring you would expect measurements to be spread more or less evenly on either side of the average value. To be more precise, with the standard deviation known, you would expect a certain proportion of measurements to fall within plus and minus one, two, and three standard deviations of the average value. If this does not occur, again there is an indication of trouble. As an example, the probability of a measurement falling above the average is, of course, 50%. The probability of two successive measures above the mean is 25% (.5 x .5). And the probability of three successive measures above the mean is 12.5% (.5 x .5 x .5). Four successive above is 6.25%, and so on. If we get to seven successive measures above the average the probability is less than 1%, and we could reasonably conclude that something strange (a special event) has taken place. The other criteria are linked with the probabilities of successive measurements falling beyond a particular number of standard deviations. A full list can be found in books on SPC.

The interpretation of process control charts is a skill that can be developed. Particular chart patterns are indicative of particular problems that may be developing. Some indications of the possibilities are given in the figure.

Process capability
Being "in control" indicates that measurements taken from items coming out of the process follow an expected pattern (the normal distribution). But being "in control" does not necessarily mean that the process is making good quality products. The process may be producing consistent products

STATISTICAL PROCESS CONTROL
Process Capability

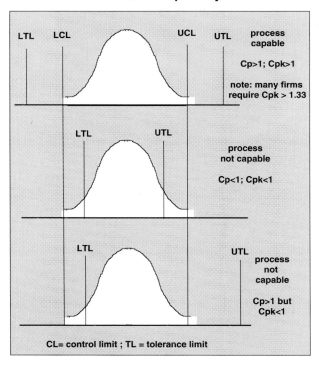

with small variation all of which are below the specification (i.e. consistently bad). So there is another requirement. This is referred to as "process capability".

Process capability refers to the match between the location of the upper and lower process control limits (UCL and LCL) and the specification limits USL and LSL (also known as tolerance limits UTL and LTL). The location of the process control limits is due to the natural variation of the process that makes the product. The specifications of the product, on the other hand, are given by the designer of the product. These are two distinctly separate things, but they must relate in order to produce quality products.

It is important that process capability should not be measured before the process is "in control". In other words, if there are assignable causes and special events to be sorted out, this must be done first. These assignable causes are by their nature unpredictable, and have an unpredictable effect on the process control measures.

Process capability is measured by two ratios "Cp" and "Cpk". The Cp measure simply compares the specification (or tolerance) spread with the process spread. Clearly if the natural spread of the process is wider than the spread of the specifications, (i.e. the Cp ratio is less than 1) then defectives are certainly going to occur. (Defectives will "seep out"; this is a way to remember the ratio names). But we need to also be concerned with where the process spread is located in relation to the specification limits. One could have a small process spread located outside of the specification limits, even though the Cp value is acceptable. So Cpk is needed.

Cpk is the smaller of two ratios :

$$\frac{(\text{upper specification limit - process average value})}{\text{half the process spread}}$$

or

$$\frac{(\text{process average value - lower specification limit})}{\text{half the process spread}}$$

Half the process spread is, of course, equal to the upper control limit minus the lower control limit. Refer to the diagrams.

In practice, many companies insist on a Cpk value of at least 1.33 before the process is regarded as "capable". So "quality capable" means that the process or machine is both "in control" and has a Cpk value of at least 1.33. As the Cpk value goes above 1.33, the likelihood of defects declines so the need to take more frequent samples decreases. So it is always a good idea to seek to improve Cpk values even if the value of 1.33 has been reached. This can be done by many means including improved maintenance, better tool wear monitoring, closer working with suppliers, and improved training.

Attribute charts : The p and c charts (see also seperate section)
It is not always possible to measure variables. Some defects, such as scratches, tears, and holes are either there or they are not. The products either pass or they do not. This is where "p" (percentage) and "c" charts come in. p Charts are used where there are batches of product and the percentage that are defective can be determined. c Charts are used where there are a number of a possible types of defect associated with a particular product, for instance the number of scratches or stains or dents on a table.

With attributes there is only one chart that is plotted, not two as with the average and range chart. But the basic concepts of controlling variation, of taking samples, of setting up the charts, and of interpreting them remain. Only the formulas are different. These are given in books on SPC.

Check Sheets

The last of the seven tools is also there to maintain the level of quality attained by the application of the previous tools. This is the straightforward yet effective tool of check sheets. A check sheet simply details the correct procedure. This correct procedure must be verified or audited at specific intervals.

There are several forms. "Aircraft style" checks would be carried out at the start of every shift or the start of each new batch, as an airline pilot would do before setting out. A process diagram, placed next to the machine or service counter, details what should be done and may advise what action to take in special circumstances.

One special form of check sheet, used by Toyota, is related to the "Seven Wastes", and is a sheet containing perhaps 50 questions that ask operators if particular events are taking place. ("Do you have to reach to grasp a control?", "Do you have to take more than two paces to collect parts?".) These are further discussed under the Seven Wastes.

Note: Some quality experts interpret Check Sheets as Tally Charts, whereby the number of occurences of an event are recorded. This is thus a form of histogram.

The 7 Wastes

Overproduction

Waiting

Transporting

Inappropriate Processing

Unnecessary Inventory

Unnecessary Motions

Defects

The 7 Wastes

The "7 Wastes" or MUDA were originally developed by Toyota's chief engineer Taiichi Ohno to neatly encapsulate all the forms of waste that occur in a manufacturing plant. Identification of waste is the first stage to its elimination. Now we recognize that use of the 7 wastes extends into service and distribution.

The 7 wastes are productivity- rather than quality-related. But quality and productivity are closely linked. Improved productivity leads to leaner operations which make quality problems more visible. And better quality improves productivity by cutting out wasteful practices such as rework, extra inspection, and all the activities associated with doing an operation for the second time. So a systematic attack on wastes is also a systematic attack on some of the underlying causes of poor quality.

The opposite of waste is value adding. By definition, any activity that does not add value for the customer is waste and should be a candidate for reduction or elimination. And any activity that does not add value for the customer can be regarded as poor quality.

The 7 wastes are a set rather than individual entities. As a set they form the core of the just-in-time philosophy, and as such they have been the subject of awareness training for operators in manufacturing. Checklists have often been developed from them. At Toyota there are waste checklists for manufacturing, distribution, and clerical operations.

The Waste of Overproduction

Ohno believed that the waste of overproduction was the most serious of all the wastes because it was the root of so many problems. Overproduction is making too much, too early or "just-in-case". It is working ahead of the production schedule, which in turn should be linked to the customer's rate of demand. The aim should be to make exactly what is required, no more and no less, just-in-time and with perfect quality. Overproduction discourages a smooth flow of goods or services. "Lumpiness" (i.e. making products or working in erratic bursts) is a force against quality and productivity. By contrast, regularity encourages a "no surprises" atmosphere which may not be very exciting but is much better management.

Overproduction leads directly to excessive lead time and storage times. As a result defects may not be detected early, products may deteriorate, and artificial pressures on work rate may be generated. All these increase the chances of defects. Taking it further, overproduction leads to excessive work-in-process inventories which lead to the physical separation of operations and the discouragement of communication.

Yet overproduction is often the natural state. People do not have to be encouraged to overproduce; they often do so "just to be safe". Often this is reinforced by a bonus system that encourages output that is not needed. By contrast, the Kanban system prevents unplanned overproduction by allowing work to move forwards only when the next work area is ready to receive it. Although kanban was made famous in manufacturing, it was originally developed from the supermarket restocking procedure and certainly has application in the service industry. (Hamburgers are only made at a rate in line with demand and clerical operations are most effective when there is a uniform flow of work.) The motto "sell daily? make daily!" is as relevant in an office as it is in a factory.

The Waste of Waiting

The waste of waiting occurs whenever time is not being used effectively. Time is an important element of competitiveness and quality. Customers do not appreciate being kept waiting but they may be prepared to pay a premium to be dealt with faster. Waiting involves a delay to non value adding activities.

In a factory, any time that materials or components are seen to be not moving (or not having value added) is an indication of waste. Waiting is the enemy of smooth flow. Although it may be very difficult to reduce waiting to zero, the goal remains. Whether the waiting is of parts in a factory or customers in a bank there should always be an awareness of a non-ideal situation and a questioning of how the situation can be improved.

When operators and employees are waiting for work or simply waiting for something to do, it is waste. Can the time not be better spent on another operation or on training, cleaning, maintaining, checking, practising changeovers or even deliberate relaxation? All of these are forces for improved quality and productivity. But they require management to have developed a contingency plan on the best use of time.

A bottleneck operation that is waiting for work is a waste. As Goldratt has pointed out in his book "The Goal", "an hour lost at a bottleneck is an hour lost for the whole plant". Effective use of bottleneck time is a key to regular production which in turn strongly influences productivity and quality.

The Waste of Transporting

Customers do not pay to have goods moved around (unless they have hired a removal service!). So any movement of materials in a factory is waste. It is a waste that can never be fully eliminated but it is also a waste that over time should be continually reduced. The number of transport and material handling operations is directly proportional to the likelihood of damage and deterioration. Double handling is a waste that affects productivity and quality.

Transporting is closely linked to communication. Where distances are long, communication is discouraged and quality may be the victim. Feedback on poor quality is inversely related to transportation length, whether in manufacturing or in services. There is increasingly the awareness that for improved quality in manufacturing or services, people from interacting groups need to be located physically closer together. For instance, the design office may be placed deliberately near the production area.

When this waste gains recognition by employees steps can be taken to reduce it. Measures include monitoring the flow lengths of products through a factory or paper through an office. The number of steps, and in particular the number of non value-adding steps, should be monitored. (This can be used as an input into various techniques such as value analysis, nominal group, or time charting.)

The Waste of Inappropriate Processing

Inappropriate processing refers to the waste of "using a hammer to crack a nut". Thinking in terms of one big machine instead of several smaller ones discourages operator "ownership", leads to pressure to run the machine as often as possible rather than only when needed, and encourages general purpose machines that may not be ideal for the need at hand. It also leads to poor layout, which as we have seen in the previous section, leads to extra transportation and poor communication. So the ideal is to use the smallest machine, capable of producing the required quality, distributed to the points of use.

Inappropriate processing also refers to machines and processes that are not quality capable. In other words, a process that cannot help but make defects. (The concept of capability is dealt with more fully under the tool of statistical process control.) In general, a capable process requires to have the correct methods, training, and tools, as well as having the required standards clearly known.

The Waste of Unnecessary Inventory

Although having no inventory is a goal that can never be attained, inventory is the enemy of quality and productivity. This is so because inventory tends to increase leadtime, prevents rapid identification of problems, and increases space thereby discouraging communication. The true cost of extra inventory is very much in excess of the money tied up in it.

"Just-in-time" (JIT) manufacturing has taught that inventory deliberately hides problems by covering them up. So, perhaps, a quality problem is not considered important because there are always extra parts available if one is defective. JIT encourages deliberate inventory reduction to uncover this sort of problem. Perhaps the safety inventory is deliberately cut. If nothing happens - fine, you have learned to operate with a leaner system. If stoppage occurs - good, because the problem has been recognized and can now be attacked at its root cause. (See the 5 Why technique on how this is done.)

The Waste of Unnecessary Motions

Unnecessary motions refers to the importance of ergonomics for quality and productivity. If operators have to stretch, bend, pick-up, move in order to see better, or in any way unduly exert themselves, the victim is immediately the operator but ultimately quality and productivity.

This is why an awareness of the ergonomics of the workplace is not only ethically desirable, but economically sound. Toyota, famous for its quality, is known to place a high importance on "quality of worklife". Toyota encourages all its employees to be aware of working conditions that contribute to this form of waste.

The Waste of Defects

Last, but not least, is the waste of defects. This one was included by Ohno to complete the set, and is the "bottom line". Defects cost money. Just how much is discussed under the technique of Cost of Quality. The Toyota philosophy is that a defect should be regarded as a challenge, as an opportunity to improve, rather than something to be traded off against what is ultimately poor management. That a defect, any defect, is a waste has much in common with the uncompromising "zero defect" view of Phil Crosby.

Other Wastes

Today, long after Ohno's classic list of wastes was first produced, we recognise other types of waste. These include the waste of human potential or talent (not "bringing your brain to work"), the waste of excess energy or power used, the waste of pollution, the waste of space, and the waste of unnecessary complexity.

Further reading
Japan Management Association, *Kanban : Just-in-Time at Toyota*, Productivity Press, 1985
Maasaki Imai, *Gemba Kaizen*, McGraw Hill, 1997, Chapter 6

The 6 New Tools

Affinity Diagram
Interrelationship Diagram
Tree Diagram
Matrix Analysis
Contingency Chart
Critical Path Analysis

Q
60

The New Tools

A working knowledge of the basic "7 Tools of Quality", described in a separate section, was considered by Ishikawa to be necessary for everyone. The "new" tools, described in this section, are not for everyone in the organisation, but should be useful to every manager, decision maker and team leader. The origin of the new 7 tools is unclear. Several have been around for a long time. But is was Mizuno who collected up seven and assembled them in a book entitled "The 7 New Quality Tools for Managers and Staff". The six new tools presented here are almost the same as those assembled by Mizuno and concentrate on the most useful ones. Like the basic 7 tools, the new tools should be thought of as a set, working together for maximum effectiveness.

The Affinity Diagram

The Affinity Diagram is a brainstorming aid used in group situations. The concept is a simple, but very effective. First a problem or issue is selected. This may be a specific issue or gut desire to improve. Then an appropriate group is assembled. A facilitator is appointed, ideally not a usual member of the group. The group brainstorms out suggestions by writing them on cards in silent generation mode. The cards are stuck up on a board. The group, now in discussion or in silent mode, works on assembling the cards into sets having an "affinity" with one another. Having rearranged and assembled them, a new card is added for each set with a brief description summarising the essential features of the group. So the output is a set of Summary Cards, one for each set of ideas. The end result is a clearer understanding of the issues involved or approaches that are possible. This tool should be used for idea generation and grouping, but not for detailed problem solving; the facilitator has to watch for this.

There seem to be several advantages: it is a participative exercise which generates commitment, it identifies commonalities in thinking within the group, and it provides a wealth of ideas which can be refined by using other tools. It is excellent for preliminary planning purposes, particularly in addressing ill-defined areas where the problem is to identify the problems. The group undertaking an Affinity Diagram task will often be an established team, but for some situations a special purpose group, ideally comprising a "diagonal slice" through the organisation, is required.

There is no one correct way, but a few suggestions follow :

* Use an external facilitator, with no "bones to pick"
* State the area clearly, even if it is not possible to state the problem
* Use 3M "Post-It" cards : one idea per card
* Have a silent generation period of 10 minutes
* Confine the card writing to a few words. Use verbs and nouns.
* Put the cards up on a flip chart in random order; don't preassemble
* Allow brief description of each idea but no discussion or criticism
* Let the facilitator assemble the first affinity sets without discussion
* Allow extra cards to be generated or cards to be rewritten
* In rearranging cards, don't allow arguments or long discussions
* It is worth spending time on the wording of Summary Cards
* Draw bold lines around the sets
* Keep the pace brisk; don't bog down in discussion.

AFFINITY and INTERRELATIONSHIP DIAGRAMS

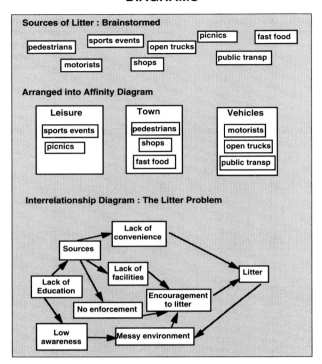

The Interrelationship or Network Diagram

An interrelationship diagram seeks to identify logical strings of connections between several problems or issues. The aim is to reach consensus about root causes, and about the sequence in which work should proceed. It helps prioritise areas to be tackled and avoids tackling inappropriate problems. People who have been involved with systems analysis (see for example the "Soft Systems Methodology") will have already used this tool. So will have project managers.

The tool can be used as a follow up from the generation of an Affinity Diagram. In this case, just begin where the team left off assembling the Affinity Diagram. There will already be logical groupings, so the task is to connect up the cards.

Alternatively, begin with a statement of the problem or issue or "Root Definition". Then brainstorm out the set of "minimum necessary activities" to address the problem or issue. Use a verb and noun in each activity. It's a good idea to use "Post-It" stickers; one per activity. (Refer to the Soft Systems methodology to check out the activities and "root definition"). Once again the task is to connect up the activities.

Yet another possibility is consider a project to be completed. First consider the major elements to be completed. (This is called "chunking"). Connect up the major chunks first. Then take each major chunk and consider the detailed activities for each. Where a project network is being considered there will be only one ending point, and usually one start point. This is not necessarily the case with interrelationship diagrams.

Many connections will be obvious. There will be a logical sequence. But one can also tackle it in a more systematic way. For each activity ask
       * which activities does the activity precede (draw an arrow to these activities)
       * which activities does the activity follow (draw an arrow from these activities)
If the activities have been written on Post-It stickers, start a new diagram on a fresh sheet and reassemble stickers where the relationships exist.

Once you have completed the diagram examine it. Look out for activities where there are several arrows coming out from them. This would indicate an important root cause. These are obvious issues or problems to tackle first. Then look out for activities where there are several activities leading into them. This may indicate an important junction, milestone, or bottleneck that also requires serious attention.

Project managers know that the process of developing a network diagram is at least as important as doing the subsequent calculations to calculate the critical path (see the Project Network tool.) So it is with interrelationship diagrams in general. Having the team discuss the nature of the connections is a valuable educational task. Invariably the team will come away from the exercise feeling that they understand a lot more about the problem or issue. They will have much better ideas on how to tackle its solution or improvement. So for quality improvement this is a super, but simple to use, tool.

The Tree Diagram

The Tree Diagram arranges goals, problems, or customer requirements in a hierarchy. It shows how a problem or goal is broken down into more detailed sub-problems or sub-goals. The breakdown into greater levels of detail can take place on several levels, until a manageable set of activities is achieved. It is similar to an organisation chart, or for those in manufacturing, like a bill of materials. That's it!

The Tree Diagram is another simple but effective tool. The only thing strange about it, is the fact that it is not used more often. It helps to break down complex issues into sub issues. It is useful in planning a new program, a new service, or a new product. It is an essential part of constructing a Quality Function Deployment matrix (see the section on QFD) where it is used to assemble the "voice of the customer".

In constructing a Tree Diagram use a team. The same comments as for Affinity Diagrams apply. Start at the top, with the overriding goal or requirement. This is the first "parent" item. Then, layer by layer, consider what actions or activities or features are necessary to achieve the parent. What are the components (or child items) of the parent? When this is complete, consider each child item as a parent and repeat for the next layer. And so on. A rule of thumb is that there should no more than about 7 sub items (child items) for each parent item.

The Tree Diagram is related to the Affinity Diagram in as far as the statement of the original problem or issue may form the highest level item, the Summary Cards would be good candidates to form the first level, and a selection of cards from those brainstormed out would probably be used at various levels within a branch under each summary card.

The Tree Diagram is really another form of Interrelationship Diagram. The difference is that in a Tree Diagram each sub activity or goal has only one "parent" or main goal on the next highest level, whereas in the Interrelationship Diagram there is no such rule so that several interconnections are possible at each level. The Interrelationship Diagram is the spaghetti, but the Tree Diagram is a carefully layered dessert with the cherry on the top.

TREE DIAGRAM and
CONTINGENCY CHART

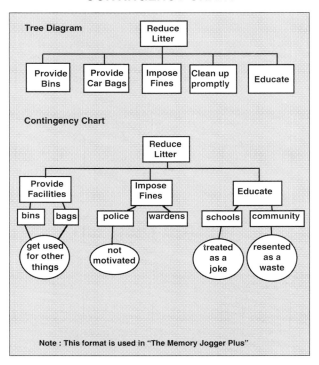

N
E
W

T
O
O
L
S

Perhaps the most difficult problem in assembling a tree diagram is to ensure that all items on each level are approximately at the same "level of resolution"; so for example a "Total Quality Programme" would normally be found on a higher level than a "SPC Programme".

Matrix Analysis

Typically, problems in quality management have several "dimensions" or interacting aspects. For instance, the problem of litter requires at least education, litter bin provision, enforcement, cleanup, and bin clearing. The problem is then to sort them out, to rank them, to separate the "vital few from the trivial many" (to quote Juran). So Matrix Analysis is a set of tools for analysing data and for decision making. There are several tools ranging from simple to quite complex. A few of the most useful versions are looked at here. Matrix analysis can be used in conjunction with several of other of the "50", but notably QFD and value analysis.

Relative Weighting

A common way to weight or indicate relative importance is to merely distribute points between the factors under consideration. This is a "gut feel" procedure, common in market research and in customer focus groups. When done with a good sample of people (say above 30) it is possible to assign confidence limits to the results. A simple and useful technique.

A Matrix for Ranking Priorities : Pairwise Comparison

Pairwise comparison forces a more systematic consideration to be made, and therefore could be regarded as more reliable than point distribution. Of course, pairwise comparison merely has a relative ranking as its outcome, not a relative weighting. Pairwise comparison typically follows an

MATRIX ANALYSIS

Example : Design of a Hamburger to Customer preferences

Begin with a Focus Group to determine Customer Requirements and relative weightings. Then :

Customer Requirements	Customer preference weighting	Features			
		Beef	Bun	Lettuce	Ketchup
Moisture	1	0 · 0	0 · 0	1 · 1	9 · 9
Flavour	3	27 · 9	0 · 0	0 · 0	9 · 3
Nutrition	3	27 · 9	9 · 3	0 · 0	0 · 0
Visual Appeal	5	45 · 9	5 · 1	5 · 1	5 · 1
Value for Money	5	45 · 9	5 · 1	0 · 0	5 · 1
Weighted scores		144	19	6	28

Conclusion : Concentrate attention on Beef and Ketchup

Note : This is the analysis performed in a QFD Matrix

Affinity exercise or Tree Diagram exercise. The starting point is a set of actions or factors which need to rearranged into ranked order. Simply arrange the actions or factors to be ranked along two sides of a square matrix, with each side having the same actions. Give each factor or action a letter, just to make data entry easier. Mark the diagonal, from top left to bottom right. The cross out all squares on the diagonal and all squares below the diagonal. You will left with a set of squares which enables each action to be compared with each other action. Now compare each action with each other action, pair by pair. Ask, firstly, for each pair, which action is the most important. If it is action A then write A in the square, and so on. If there is no clear difference or priority, leave the square blank. Repeat for all squares. Then, secondly, for all filled in squares, ask by how much does the chosen factor have priority over the second factor. If significantly different, give a score of 9 points. If only marginally, give a score of 3. Write the numbers in the squares. When all squares have been completed, add up the scores associated with each letter. The resulting scores represent the ranking. Very often you would find one or two really dominant actions or factors, and several with lower scores. This is normal and desirable.

Two Dimensional Weighting

In, for example, Quality Function Deployment, but also in many other areas of quality management it is necessary to relate means to ends or "whats" to "hows". In QFD the "whats" are customer requirements and the "hows" are product features. To start, there will typically be a set of weighted or ranked "whats", derived by a method such as relative weighting. As for "hows", many product characteristics serve more than one purpose, for instance the meat in a hamburger provides nutrition, flavour, and bulk. The same can be said for a training programme which may provide skills, motivation and retain staff.

The problem is how to give weights or a ranking to the "hows", so that they reflect the "whats". Begin by constructing a matrix : whats in rows against hows in columns. The whats will usually be weighted, so add an extra column to reflect these weights. Now go through the matrix, cell by cell. For each, ask to what extent the how is able to meet the what. (eg. To what extent does the meat in a hamburger meet the requirement for nutrition?). The answer is high (write in 9 points), medium (write in 3 points), low (write in 1 point), or not at all (write in zero). In some cases a negative is possible (write in minus 3). Then, for each cell, multiply the point score by the weight for that row (i.e. for that "what"). Write this figure in the top right hand of the cell. Lastly, add up the top right hand figures for each column (i.e. for each "how"). This gives a weighting which reflects the ability of each "how" to meet each "what".

The applications of this method are very wide. Apart from product design through QFD, other applications are selecting what sub-programmes are to be implemented as part of a Total Quality programme, selecting suppliers, and selecting between several locations for a new factory.

Multi Dimensional Matrices

Multi Dimensional Matrices are a whole class of matrices which allow data to be analysed in several dimensions. Of course, strictly a matrix can compare only two factors at a time, but the inclusion of additional factors can add insight. The possibilities are vast. Please refer to the figures.

Two Dimensional matrices can show, for example, defects against operator; or complaints against shift.

Three Dimensional matrices can show, for example, defects against operator and time; or complaints against shift and location.

Four Dimensional matrices can show, for example, defects against operator and time, as well as giving additional relating to products; or complaints against shift and location as well as giving additional data on tasks performed.

In all case the cells of the matrices can contain numerical data or symbols to indicate high, medium, low or nil.

The last two of the "new" 7 tools are particularly relevant for project management. Of course, project management is not unique to Quality Management, but without good project management the implementation of Total Quality is impossible.

Contingency Chart or Decision Tree

The Contingency Chart helps to map the risks associated with the implementation of a plan. The chart looks similar to a Tree Diagram, except that on each layer all the alternatives to achieving the goal on the layer above are given. In the language used for the tree diagram, a parent is a statement of the goal and the child items are the alternatives. A child item on one level can also be a parent to levels below. Having established the tree, contingencies can be specifically considered.

Like much in project management the real value lies in the team-based process which considers alternatives beforehand. Too often project management concentrates on the mechanical aspects of activities and time, rather than on people and risk. The Contingency Chart helps to correct the balance. Both the Contingency Chart and the last of the new 7 tools (discussed next) are necessary for good project management.

Managers familiar with decision theory will recognise that we are talking about a "decision tree". In a proper decision tree, however, probabilities are assigned to each option, and a calculation made as to the path of least cost. This degree of sophistication is not considered necessary in a Contingency Chart; in fact more emphasis is placed on thinking though the alternatives than in doing the calculations.

So the Contingency Chart amounts to sequential brainstorming followed by evaluation. Begin with the overall goal; write this at the top. Then the team brainstorms out alternative ways of getting there. These form the first level of the chart. Then each alternative is considered, and once again the team brainstorms out alternatives. These are written in under each major alternative. Continue in this way until the team considers that sufficient detail has been covered. This is normally two, or unusually three, levels down from the goal. An alternative to the first step is to list the major activities necessary to reach the goal. Thereafter the method proceeds as before.

After sufficient alternatives have been generated, a final level is brainstormed. This contains, for each alternative, a set of things that could go wrong or the more likely possibilities. Of course, there are many things that could go wrong, but the team should consider only major or most likely events. The difference between alternatives and things that can go wrong are that the former are choices under ones own control, but the latter are chance events or uncertainties. (The same distinction is found in decision trees).

Now the team should consider the consequences of each branch. What are the risks? What are the advantages? There are no rules how to do this; the value lies in the discussion. After discussion the best alternative should emerge, but the real value is having thought through the alternatives and their risks in advance. There should be few major unexpected events, and however the uncertainty turns out, the Contingency Chart should have ensured that most eventualities have been covered. "Forewarned is forearmed".

Critical Path Analysis

Critical Path Analysis (CPA) is a long established tool for project management. Project Management is a vital part of any quality implementation and is often fairly poorly managed. But of course CPA is not confined to Quality. CPA is useful to schedule resource usage in any environment. Today there is abundant inexpensive software for CPA and its extensions, and you should seldom need to calculate a network. But be warned: DO NOT get carried away by sophisticated software; most features will not be required. And DO use the Contingency Chart in conjunction with CPA.

CPA aims at establishing the time needed for a project, what the critical activities are, and what the expected start and finish times are for each activity. It uses a network of arrows or nodes to establish the logical order of activities. The real value of CPA is in drawing the network, not in the subsequent calculations.

(The method to be described below is known as "activity on node". This is becoming the standard. An older alternative is known as "activity on arrow". In the latter case "dummy" activities are sometimes required. Detail is to be found in numerous textbooks, if you require it.)

Begin by listing all the activities (verb plus noun) that are necessary for the project. Try to keep these at a high level; you can add sub-networks later. Post-it stickers are a good idea for flexibility. Each activity should have an estimated time. Put each activity in a square. Then arrange the activities into logical order by connecting them up with arrows. The rule is : no activity can start before its predecessor activity is complete. If activities can run in parallel do not arrange them in sequence. There should be one start activity and one end activity and no circular loops. Recall that getting the network right (i.e. thinking through the project in advance) is the major benefit. Use a team if possible.

CRITICAL PATH ANALYSIS (CPA)

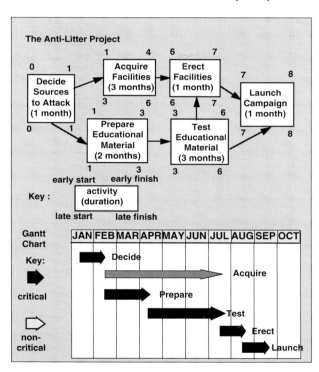

N
E
W

T
O
O
L
S

To calculate times, a CPA network requires a "forward pass" and a "backward pass"; both are simple. Begin the forward pass at time 0. This is the "early start" time for the first activity. "Early start" is the earliest time that an activity can start; "early finish" is the earliest time that an activity can be completed by, and is equal to the early start time plus the duration of the activity. Write in the early start time of each activity on the top left hand corner of the activity square, and the early finish time on the top right hand of the square. The early finish of each activity becomes the early start time of the next activity. Where there are two or more immediate predecessor activities, take the greater of the finish dates of the predecessors because all must be complete before the activity can begin. Move through the whole network doing this calculation activity by activity. The early finish of the last activity is the minimum project duration.

Now begin the backward pass. The early finish of the last activity will also be the "late finish" of that activity ("late finish" is the latest time that an activity can finish by whilst not delaying the completion of the entire project. "late start" is the latest time that an activity can start without delaying the whole project. Write in the late finish on the bottom right hand of each activity square, and the late start on the bottom left of the activity square.) Begin with the late finish time for the last activity. The late start for each activity equals the late finish minus the duration. Now move backwards through the network. The late start of an activity becomes the late finish of its predecessor activity in all cases except where there are two or more immediate subsequent activities. In this case take the smaller of late start dates of the immediate subsequent activities as the late finish for the activity. (Since there are several subsequent activities it is the earliest of the late starts that will govern). At the end of the backward pass you should end with an late start time for the first activity of zero; if not you have made a mistake.

You have now established, for each activity, the "early start". "early finish", "late start", and "late finish". The "slack" or additional free time for each activity equals (late finish - early finish) or (late start - early start). These should give the same result. Some activities, forming a continuous path through the network, will have zero slack. This is the critical path. Any delay along the critical path will delay the whole project; it follows that these are the activities to monitor most closely.

To aid communication, it is a good idea to show the planned early start, early finish and late finish dates on a bar chart for each activity.

As the project proceeds, monitor progress, update the times, update the network if necessary, and redo the calculation. It is nice to have a computer to do this for you.

References:
Shigeru Mizuno (ed), *Management for Quality Improvement : The 7 New QC Tools*, Productivity Press, 1988
Michael Brassard, *The Memory Jogger Plus*, GOAL/QPC, 1989

The Techniques

5 S
Benchmarking
Best Demonstrated Practice
Cost of Quality
c and u charts
Cusums
Cycle of Service
Data Presentation
Design of Experiments
Failure Modes and Effect
Analysis (FMEA)
Five Whys
Force Field Analysis
Hoshin
Importance Performance Matrix
Kaizen

Q
60

Market Survey and Customer
 Observation
Moments of Truth
Nominal Group Technique
 (NGT)
Precontrol
Quality Function Deployment
Relationships and Encounters
Service Blueprinting
Service Gaps and SERVQUAL
Service Profit Chain
Service Recovery
Six Sigma
Sixth Sigma
Supplier Partnerships
Yield Management

Q
60

5 S

The 5 S concept has been associated with Total Productive Maintenance (TPM) and workplace management in manufacturing for some time. However, it is now being used in services also. 5 S is fundamental to quality and productivity. It is the foundation stone.

The 5 S's stem from 5 Japanese words. It is a name that has stuck, despite the fact that few English speakers understand the Japanese words. However, there is an English equivalent of the 5 S's which more or less mean the same thing. There is also the 5 C's covering the same ground. So here are the 5 S's Japanese, 5 S's English, 5 C's, and English ordinary :

Seiri, Sort, Cleanup
Seiton, Straighten (or Simplify), Configure, Orderliness or Organisation
Seiso, Scrub (or Sweep), Clean and check regularly, Maintenance
Seiketsu, Standardise, Conformity
Shitsuke, Self Discipline, Custom and Practice, Training and Routine

All this may sound draconian, but is in fact the basis of quality and productivity in factory and office. As Taiichi Ohno, Toyota's legendary innovator of the JIT system said, "Management begins at the workplace".

Cleanup is about removing all items (especially accumulated dirt and grime, but also inventory, paper, furniture, tools, memos, manuals, rubbish, filing cabinets, etc) that are not required or are unnecessary within a period ahead. Such items are waste, or lead to waste. They take up space, lead to extra walking around, and lead to waste of time whilst searching for needed items buried under piles of less important material. An office example is the "clean desk" policy run by several companies, requiring employees to have a clear desk at the end of each day. In the office beware of paperwork that is shuffled, re-read, and searched through often several times per day. It's all waste. Cleanup also includes fixing : any tools or equipment that is broken or not calibrated must either be thrown away or repaired : decide which, and act.

According to some 5S enthusiasts, one can make a judgment on the status of productivity and quality within seconds of walking into a factory, office, or warehouse. Beware!

There are two approaches. One is to begin with a longer period (say 6 months) and to clear all that is not foreseen to be used within that period; then to reduce the period until you are working with only (say) this week's items. The other approach is to "red tag" items where there is uncertainty. The item is not removed but the tag indicates when it was tagged and if found be unused for a specified period (6 months?) is either thrown out or removed to a storage location. Inventory, of course, is also a candidate for red tagging : don't forget stillages in the second row. P.S. Resist the temptation to red tag the supervisor!

Orderliness is the well known (but probably less well implemented) "a place for everything and everything in its place". Orderliness should be the next step after cleanup. The idea is to minimise waste (see the "7 Wastes"). It is really about having things easy to hand, labelled, classified, and easily visible. Shadow boards may be used for tools, books arranged by topic, shelves not too high, wheels on carts, heavy low and light high, colour coded connections and pipes, and so on. It is also about inventory : having specific locations for specific parts, perhaps painted squares, and of course a limit on excessive parts delivered lineside too early. When combined with cleanup, this lays the foundation for the kanban system.

Orderliness has a direct impact on productivity : searching for lost papers and tools should be eliminated. And time wasted should be cut by careful location of tools and materials. Do a Pareto in order to locate the most frequently used items close by. It may be possible to incorporate some failsafing : cords attached to tools, racking or slots which do not hold other than the correct tool.

Clean and check regularly is of course about keeping things clean and ready to go. This step follows cleanup and orderliness. The important point is that this is not delegated to some cleaner, but is done for oneself, on a regular ongoing basis. It needs to be done daily. It is about pride. Workplaces can never be too clean. Cleanliness extends to non-seen areas : machines need to be clean inside and out - in fact, making the innards of machines visible by using transparent covers is desirable. Routine maintenance may be incorporated : oil every day, replace after 5000 sheets, and "aircraft style checks" where items are checked at the start of every shift (have you ever been into a bank to discover a non-working pen chained to the counter?). One important activity is identifying which maintenance activities are the responsibility of the ordinary staff, and which are the responsibility of specialist maintenance staff. Responsibility for the photocopier is good example; clearly define who is responsible for what : secretaries, staff, specialists.

(A note in passing : one reason for Japanese success at quality is said to be their natural obsession for cleanliness. Most Japanese regularly visit the "onsen" or hot spring bath, take at least one bath per day (many women take two per day) but scrub before getting into the bath - lying in dirty, soapy water is a no-no.)

Standardise refers to engendering the HABIT of workplace procedures. It is about the establishment and maintenance of standards. The first standard is to ensure that the previous 3 S's are in place and maintained. Then there is the discipline of work itself. Despite what some people think about Frederick Taylor, there is one best way to do any task which will minimise time and effort, and maximise quality and productivity. To some this may sound like boring repetition, but job interest should not be confused with the best way to do it. Standards establish the foundation for further improvement. They are part of the Deming cycle of Plan, Do, Check, Act or Standardise. Also included in this category is the routine of health and safety : making it the habit to wear safety glasses, gloves, and ear plugs.

Standards should be kept lineside and be diagrammatic (first preference) or written. Never verbal. Standard procedures can be colour coded to match the product which carries a label of matching colour. When an engineering change occurs, a number on the product should match the number on the standard sheet.

Any standard should cover not only what to do when things are normal, but also what to do if things go wrong.

Discipline is to make sure that the activities are kept going. This amounts to identifying responsible people, setting the frequency of review (the previous steps won't last forever), and maintaining a visual record for important equipment. Management has an important role to play here. Prevention is the watchword. But even better than prevention is failsafing (or "pokayoke" see section on Shingo), whereby inspection is automatic and a warning occurs. Examples are automatic counts on cutting, showing a light when tool change is required, or automatic backup of hard disk. One way is to establish regularity of procedures. Nissan does a 60 point check every week. Checklists are gone through at the beginning of every shift, and charts completed at the end. Another may be incentives : a prize for the best workplace. These principles are as applicable in service as in manufacturing.

Management participation and interest is of course vital to keep a 5 S programme going. Expectation and example are important. Management must be seen to practise 5 S themselves, and to maintain commitment.

Dramatic savings often result when 5 S is introduced. It is the basis of "kaikaku" or "instant revolution" described by Womack and Jones in their book "Lean Thinking" and by Joynson in "Sid's Heroes" (who claims 30% improvement in productivity in 2 days!).

Further reading
Hiroyuki Hirano, *5 Pillars of the Visual Workplace,* Productivity Press, Portland, OR, 1995.
Hiroyuki Hirano, *5 S for Operators*, Productivity Press, Portland, OR, 1996
James Womack and Daniel Jones, *Lean Thinking*, Simon and Schuster, New York, 1996
Sid Joynson, *Sid's Heroes*, BBC, London, 1995

Benchmarking

The Benchmarking Centre defines Benchmarking as "the continuous, systematic search for, and implementation of, best practices which lead to superior performance". In essence it aims to compare the performance of critical processes with leading achievers. It is a guideline to what is necessary in present performance and to future requirements if the organization is to be "world class". It is about knowing yourself and really knowing the competition - where they are weak, where they are strong, and where they are going. To an extent, benchmarking is an alternative to "cost plus" budgeting, and to productivity targeting by simply "matching inflation". It is outward looking rather than inward looking. It is concerned with tracking performance, not just taking snapshots. Think of the ongoing Deming Cycle. And like several other techniques discussed here it is equally applicable to products and to services.

Of course, benchmarking is not new. People and organizations have always compared themselves to others. Juran quotes the example of how, early in the 20th century, German generals visited the Barnum and Bailey circus to study the world-renowned methods it used to move materials and animals from city to city. But it was the Xerox corporation that appears to have pioneered "competitive benchmarking". It was the systematic and comprehensive way in which Xerox set about making benchmarking a competitive weapon that has brought this technique into prominence. Robert Camp of Xerox is responsible for much of the thinking, and has written the definitive book.

Types of benchmarking include Internal (where one branch is compared with others - see the section on Best Demonstrated Practice), Competitive (as per Xerox, comparing with the toughest competitors), Functional (where similar processes are compared inside of your industry but not with direct competitors - say room service in two non-competing hotels), Generic or Process (where basic processes found in any business, such as recruitment or billing, are compared), and Performance (where measures (typically on cost, quality, delivery, reliability, and response) are compared.

Benchmarking can be seen not just as a technique on its own, but as one of a mutually reinforcing family. The insights from benchmarking are useful if not necessary for quality function deployment. For value management it can help identify what is technically possible. It is powerful as a force for change when used in force field analysis. It identifies on which of Garvin's dimensions of quality a competitor is competing. And systematic measurement is part of any quality improvement process, such as the Deming cycle or the Juran Trilogy.

We begin with the understanding that a single measure of performance is rarely adequate. Just as several instruments are necessary to monitor and control the performance of a car or plane, so it is with any organization. Now recognize that to be competitive in quality and productivity, steady inward-looking progress may not be enough. But of course one does not go out to benchmark everything possible. It must be a directed search. Robert Camp proposes using a process control model (involving inputs, process, outputs, feedback, and results) and suggests that all these are benchmarking candidates, and that "step zero", where time and care is spent considering the purpose of the exercise is most important. Camp has a 10 step approach covering planning (covering what, whom, and how), analysis (where the current and future gaps are determined), integration (involving communication and revision of goals), action (where actions are developed, then monitored, and benchmarks recalibrated).

What to measure

Robert Camp states that benchmarking is "first a goal setting process". You have to know what to benchmark, and, as with much of quality management, this brings you right back to the customer. Identify who are your customers, present and future. Now you can begin to assess their needs and the necessary core processes. These are the areas where the organization absolutely needs to perform well, and areas where unique advantages can be obtained. (Garvin's dimensions are useful as an aid). The areas can be assembled by a team using the nominal group technique (see the section on NGT) and the Affinity Diagram (see the New Tools).

There may be a particular interest in targeting areas that are known to be important, such as costs or complaints or geographical areas. Staff policies, salaries, and personnel policies on training, recruitment, and the use of people at work may be relevant. There may well be some standard productivity or quality measures in the industry. Beware of being too specific on what should be measured - there may be "more than one way to skin a cat". The idea is to concentrate on processes first and measures of performance second. With what it is you wish to benchmark now known, the next step is to identify who to benchmark.

BENCHMARKING

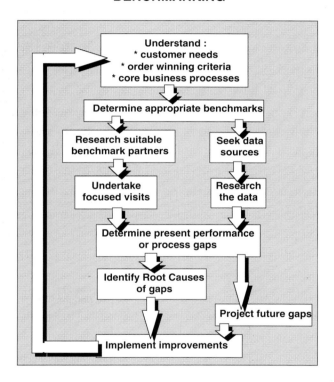

It is a good idea to think through the information collection procedure, in particular who will be responsible and where will it be centred. The latter has to be clearly communicated so that if information is obtained from or by an unexpected source, it will still go to the right place. It will often be necessary to dedicate people, part time or short term, to information collection.

Who to measure

The aim of competitive benchmarking is to find the "industry best" performance, and where appropriate the "world best" performance. The toughest competitors now and in future are often known or easy to short-list, so a search can be more focused. But do not close minds to the possibility of world class performance from a new or unexpected source. Benchmarking is an ongoing process. In Xerox, benchmarking is known of throughout the company and a "little red book" on benchmarking has been widely issued. For non competitive benchmarking the services of organisations such as the Benchmarking Centre can be used to pinpoint benchmarking partners.

How to measure

Internal benchmark information is relatively easy to obtain. Now comes the external information. There is a huge number of potential sources of benchmark information. But it must be ethically collected and secured (The Benchmarking Centre has a code of conduct including legality, exchange (give and take, not just take), confidentiality (not publishing or passing on ideas to third party competitors), and use). For competitive benchmarking some possibilities are: a library database search, commercial press cutting databases, specialist industry reviews in newspapers or journals, specialist surveys (eg by "The Economist Intelligence Unit"), trade magazines, conference papers and proceedings (managers love to tell of their achievements at such events.), market research, special surveys, factory visits and evening meetings of relevant societies, annual financial reports and published accounts, trade and sales literature, quotations from the companies themselves, management consultants and academics (who may be prepared to disclose general information while disguising names). Several authors have made the point that benchmarking is not "industrial tourism" (just visiting), nor is there any point in visiting companies that are in such a totally different league of organisation or technology that there is no chance of catching up.

Many benchmarking exercises will involve actual use of competitor products, including one-way viewing through mirrors of customer usage, and full technical disassembly.

Using benchmarks

Benchmarking is not static. It aims at projecting future trends. So when the internal and external benchmarks are assembled, analysts can begin to assess the critical question of whether the "gap" between own and competitor performance is widening or narrowing. This leads to the establishment of areas for priority action. Competitive benchmarking can become a management philosophy in itself, with the attempt being to remain or achieve "industry best" position in the particular niches identified as important. As soon as one set of improvements has been implemented, it all begins again. It's the Deming cycle.

Further reading

Robert Camp, *Benchmarking*, ASQC Quality Press, 1989
Gary Jacobson and John Hillkirk, *Xerox : American Samurai*, Macmillan, 1986
Gregory Watson, *The Benchmarking Workbook*, Productivity Press, 1992
Robert C. Camp, *Business Process Benchmarking*, ASQC Quality Press, 1995

Web sites

The Benchmarking Exchange on http://www.benchnet.com
The Benchmarking Centre on http://www.benchmarking.co.uk
American Productivity and Quality Centre on http://www.apqc.org
http://www.best-in-class.com/benchmarkingbook.htm

TECHNIQUES

Best Demonstrated Practice

Best Demonstrated Practice (BDP) is a form of internal Benchmarking. It assembles the best features of several operations to create a benchmark of a theoretical operation comprising the best features of each. For instance, in an insurance company one branch may have the best life policy service, another branch the best walk-in service, a third the best postal response time. So the best theoretical branch could comprise the best demonstrated practice from each.

Assuming that an organisation has several similar operations, the steps are as follows :

* Establish the prime measure of interest. For quality, this may be response time or queue time, a customer satisfaction measure, or a defect level, error rate, or number of complaints. For costs the measure could be contribution level, a resource utilisation level, or a comparable cost such as personnel cost per square metre. The measures should be measurable without much controversy. These measures should be carefully chosen, often in association with representative staff from operations, and be related to corporate objectives.

* Establish a suitable measure or measures against which to analyse the prime measure. Examples may be number of customers or products, sales or turnover, or size or area of operation.

* Plot the graph and analyse with branch representatives. Examples are shown. Usually an envelope or lower bound will be formed. This represents the best demonstrated practice. These are the locations to learn from. And operations furthest from the line should get attention: What special problems do they have? What are the causes? After discussion the group may conclude that there are subgroups involved within which it is possible to learn, and that nothing can be learned by comparing some locations with others.

BEST DEMONSTRATED PRACTICE

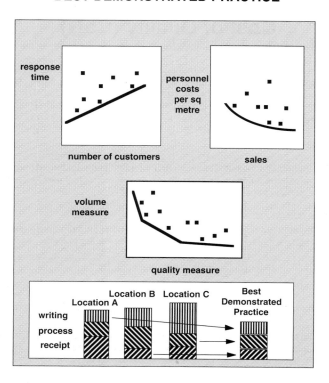

BDP is applicable in decentralised operations where there are several branches, offices or outlets providing approximately the same products or services. It is particularly useful where, in addition, there are no external benchmarks. The approach has been used for both quality improvement and cost reduction. A more sophisticated version of BDP known as Data Envelopment Analysis, which enables analysis beyond two dimensions to be undertaken, relies on linear programming. This mathematical technique is often not warranted because of data uncertainties when an approximation is good enough and has presentational difficulties. The real challenge lies in acceptance of the findings and participation in the analysis, both of which are inhibited by sophisticated mathematics.

BDP can be used in conjunction with several other techniques in this book, such as flowcharting (to better understand the process), SPC (to identify branches that are operating beyond the control limits), and Sixth Sigma (to learn from the best). The technique can also be seen as an extension of one of the "Seven Tools", namely the scatter diagram. It should not be used as a "big stick" by management to chase apparent laggards but rather to explore reasons for deviation and opportunities for improvement and learning.

Reference:
Michael Norman and Barry Stoker, *Data Envelopment Analysis,* Wiley, 1991

Cost of Quality (CoQ)

Cost of quality aims at the financial quantification of all activities involved in the prevention and rectification of defects. The idea is that if the locations and magnitudes of quality related costs are measured and brought to the attention of management, this will be a powerful force for directed improvement. Cost of quality analysis may range from one-off estimates to a complete parallel accounting system. Traditionally, quality is measured by a series of ratios. The problem is that these are seldom comprehensive and lack common units. Ratios should be supplemented by costs, which should be publicised throughout the organization. CoQ can provide specific cost justification data for a management pondering the question of quality "hype" against quality benefit.

If your organization is considering implementing cost of quality in a comprehensive way, it would be advisable to obtain the British Standard (BS 6143) "Guide to the economics of quality prevention", or the various guides published by the American Society for Quality Control. What follows are some general principles.

The conventional quality costing categories are:

* **prevention costs** : the costs of measures to prevent defects from taking place. This would include training, "pokayoke" (see Shingo), and capability studies and improvement (see SPC).

* **appraisal costs** : costs incurred in the detection of defects. This would include testing and inspection.

* **internal failure costs** : all failure costs incurred by internal customers. The costs incurred to rectify defects and failures internally, before the product or service reaches an external customer. This includes costs of scrap, rework, and all internal activities incurred through "not getting it right first time".

* **external failure costs** : all failure costs incurred by external customers. The costs incurred to rectify products and services after they have reached external customers, including returns, warranty claims, complaints, field repair, and perhaps lost custom.

Phil Crosby groups the first two referring to them as "POC" (price of conformance) and the second two as "PONC" (price of nonconformance). For simplicity we can refer to the first two as "prevention costs" and the second two as "failure costs".

Traditionally, prevention and failure costs have been seen as a trade-off. This is shown in the figure. Total costs are the sum of failure costs and prevention costs. Failure costs are thought to decline steadily, perhaps linearly, as quality improves. But as the defect level decreases, particularly as it nears 0% or perfect quality, prevention costs begin to rise very steeply, perhaps exponentially. The result is that there is an "optimal" quality level, where total costs are minimized, which is below perfect quality (or above 0% defects). This trade-off thinking is now considered to be dangerous; it means that perfect quality is not only not the aim but actually undesirable. It becomes the excuse for seeking to "get it right first time".

COST of QUALITY

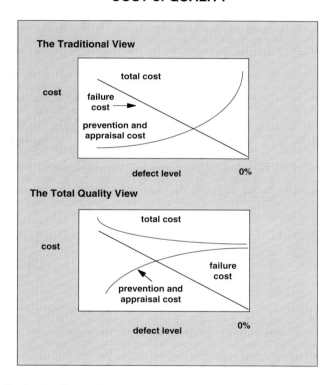

The total quality view is different. This is shown in the next figure. Here while failure costs continue to decline steadily, prevention costs tend to level out, at least above a certain level. The belief is that with "total quality" everyone participates, quality becomes the natural way of life and not an "extra", prevention requires initial but not continuing investment, and as a result costs stabilize. Total costs continue to decline all the way to the level of zero defects, so that the optimal is reached with perfect quality.

These diagrams are conceptual and have seldom been proved or disproved in practice. One point in favour of the total quality view is that the costs of failure are really unknown in terms of lost reputation and future custom. Therefore, if anything, failure costs are understated and may at least match the prevention costs. But perhaps this is all academic.

The real point is that cost of quality analysis does set out to quantify what poor quality actually costs. The results, in many organizations that have implemented CoQ, are often "shock treatment". The cost of not getting it right first time is typically in the range of 20% to 25% of turnover. So the savings that can be achieved by improving quality are very large, and the associated investment often more cost effective than the costs of increasing turnover - including marketing and capacity acquisition.

CoQ pinpoints the sources of quality costs. Specific budgets can then be set and controlled. Juran, the early pioneer of cost of quality, sees CoQ as an essential feature of his "trilogy" (see the section on Juran). So quality becomes a closely managed function, using money (the "language of management" according to Juran), rather than having quality as something that is desirable and "nice" but, when it comes to the point, really of low priority.

Some more advanced CoQ systems now incorporate cross coding, so that some of the costs that are booked into the normal costing system are cross linked to appropriate CoQ categories. This is not an exact science, and many of the problems that bedevil cost accounting (such as the appropriate allocation of overheads) are to be found in CoQ also. But exactness is not the issue, it is the trends, approximate magnitude, and locations that are important. When setting up these parallel costing systems it is useful to go further than just prevention and failure costs by identifying the source of the defect; operator error, equipment problem, material problem, specification problem, procedural problem, supplier problem or communication problem.

Many organizations do not yet undertake CoQ on a regular ongoing basis. Instead they rely on specific CoQ assessment studies. Here detailed questioning is the norm, usually making use of the process diagram, Pareto analysis, Ishikawa diagram, and histogram. (See the 7 tools.)

CoQ can be seen as closely related to the "7 Wastes". The real aim is not merely to keep on reducing the costs of (poor) quality but to go on reducing the costs of all wastes. Defects are but one of the seven wastes. Some companies have now begun to cost more wastes, either directly or through new cost accounting systems such as "activity based costing" (ABC).

Further reading
* BS 6143 (Part 2, 1990 and Part 1, 1991), British Standards Institution.
* ASQC, "Guide for Reducing Quality Costs", 1987.

"c" and "u" Charts

A "c" chart is used to monitor the number of nonconformities per product. Examples are the number of complaints per period, the number of scratches per tabletop, or the number of errors per processed document. In such cases a percentage figure is less meaningful, so a P chart cannot be used. "c" charts are particularly useful in service situations, and are instantly usable because the formula is simple enough to remember and quick to apply.

To use a c chart, the number of units sampled should be approximately the same. The control limits for a c chart are at :

$$c +/- 3\sqrt{c}$$

where c is the average value per sample. So if the average number of scratches per sample of 10 tables is 16, then the control limits are at $(16 + 3 \times 4) = 28$ and $(16 - 12) = 4$. Therefore if 30 scratches are detected, the process is out of control. Such an easy to calculate control limit should be known to every service manager to monitor, for example, the number of complaints in a week or the number of nonconformities in a sample of 10 hotel room make-ups or the number of late deliveries. Simply find the average number of complaints, take the square root of the average number, and add three times the square root to the average to give the control limit. A significant change has occurred if the number of complaints or nonconformities exceeds this control limit. The only condition to be aware of in using this fast check is that the "population" or units on which this data is gathered is approximately the same. For example, you can use the formula if the hotel occupancy is approximately constant, or the total number of deliveries is about the same. If not, use the following modification :

Where the number of units is not constant, simply replace "c" by "u" where $u = c/n$ and n is the number of units. The control limit formula is then

$$u +/- 3\sqrt{(u/n)}$$

CUSUM Charts

A "Cusum" or Cumulative Sum Chart is a type of control chart which is particularly useful for detecting small but significant changes in the process. Take a look at the conventional control chart shown and the corresponding cusum chart. Notice that the change is almost undetectable in the control chart, but is very clear on the cusum chart. A large change, on the other hand, is easy to detect on a conventional control chart.

CUSUMS

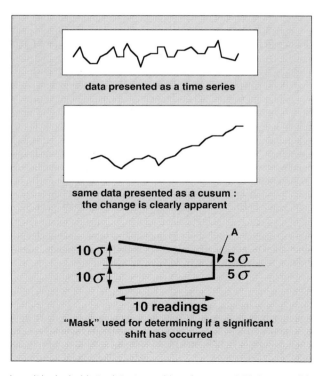

data presented as a time series

same data presented as a cusum :
the change is clearly apparent

10 readings

"Mask" used for determining if a significant
shift has occurred

T
E
C
H
N
I
Q
U
E
S

Any situation where it is desirable to detect a sudden change quickly is a candidate for a cusum. Examples are customer enquiries, fuel consumption (an excellent indicator that something has gone wrong with your car or van), yield from a chemical process, response times, or failure rates.

To plot a cusum, merely subtract the average (or target) value of the process from the actual measurement, add the resulting number to the previously accumulated number, and plot it on the chart.That is :

1.   actual measurement in period t - average value = difference for period t
2.   cusum value for period t = cusum value for last period + difference for period t

With conventional control charts, control limits are needed to detect if a real change has taken place. With a Cusum, a V Mask is used. To construct a V Mask you need to first calculate the standard deviation of the process. This will require a minimum of, say, 10 readings. (Many calculators have a key for the standard deviation). Then, draw the V Mask, as shown on the figure, on a transparent sheet. Lay the V Mask with point A, or the head, over the latest reading as shown. A change is significant if the cusum line crosses one of the trailing arms.

Further readings :

BS5703, *Guide to Data Analysis and Quality Control using Cusums*, Parts 1 to 4, British Standards Institution, Milton Keynes, 1982
J. Murdoch, *Control Charts*, Macmillan, London 1979, ISBN 0-333-26411-8

Cycle of Service and Customer Processing

Albrecht and Zemke originated the concept of a Cycle of Service, but the idea has been added to by Mahesh and by Vandermerwe. The Customer Processing concept is a variation, developed by Johnston.

A Cycle of Service (C of S) is much like a flowchart but has the important distinction of being written from the perspective of the customer, and is the sequence of events or "Moments of Truth" (MoT) (see section on this topic) experienced by the customer in dealing with the organisation. After all, as Vandermerwe suggests, value is associated with the customer, but providers only accumulate costs. As the name suggests, a C of S is normally shown on a circle. A flowchart shows the progress of a document or product, a cycle of service shows the events experienced by a customer. It is simple but effective.

The best way to draw up a cycle of service is to physically track a customer as he or she moves through a service process. Of course, not all customers will experience the same Moments of Truth, so several customer experiences may have to be combined. Where customer tracking is not possible, a team of front line employees should participate in drawing up the chart. It is best to use the verb plus noun rule in drawing up a C of S chart : for instance, "receive notice", "join queue", and the like.

Then analysis begins. Points of dissatisfaction are identified. The value of the C of S is that, perhaps for the first time, the complete sequence of events as experienced by the customer, is seen. A useful starting point is the "PETS" framework : ask if, for each moment of truth, if the Procedure is known, if the Equipment is suitable or capable of doing the job, if Training has been adequate, and if Standards are in place. Some of the MoTs will be more important than others, and will require much more attention. Where necessary, any MoT can be further broken down into a greater level of detail. For instance, the MoT "receive bank balance", can be broken down into "wait for chit", "receive chit from teller", "open chit", "read balance and other information".

Thereafter the Kano model is extremely useful. (See the section on Kano). Ask, for each MoT, what are the Basics, the Performance factors, and possible Delighters. This is a useful way of undertaking systematic analysis of weaknesses and of opportunities. The section on the Kano model emphasised that the identification of the three Kano factors is not necessarily trivial; good analysis and insight may only be gained by detailed observation.

In addition we can consider how or if each MoT can be failsafed (see the section on Shingo or Pokayoke). Recall the methods of failsafing : by contact (a height barrier in a car park), by fixed value (an airline meal tray with indentations), and by motion step (a customer number at a supermarket "deli" to ensure first come first serve).

CYCLE of SERVICE :
Car Service Example

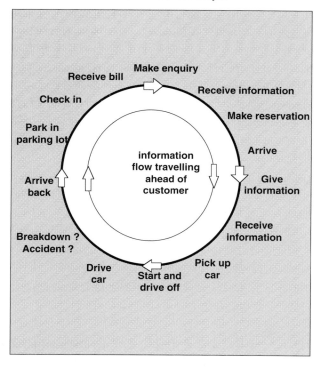

Sandra Vandermerwe's version of C of S is referred to as the Customer Activity Cycle (or CAC). This has the extension of considering "Pre", "During", and "Post" activities. Vandermerwe makes the point that customer's experiences span three stages : deciding what to do, doing it, and keeping it going and updating it. This is therefore a more powerful version because it is not limited to the actual service encounter itself. The tool acts as an agitation and educational device according to Vandermerwe. She refers to discontinuities in the flow of the cycle as "value gaps", a phrase which suggests that closing such gaps may find the framework suggested by Zeithaml et al (see the section on SERVQUAL) useful. As with the breakdown of the C of S into a hierarchy of detail, the CAC has "primary cycles", "dependent cycles" and "sub cycles".

JOHNSTON'S CUSTOMER PROCESSING OPERATION

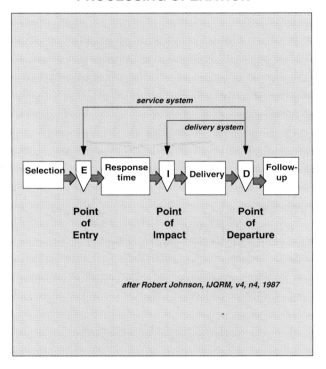

after Robert Johnson, IJQRM, v4, n4, 1987

The Johnston variation (known as the "customer processing operation" or CPO) is not shown as a cycle or a map but rather as a framework or checklist. The elements are useful in clarifying the stages, and could easily be incorporated in the previous C of S approaches. The elements are:

Selection:	when the customer decides between competing services.
Point of entry:	the initial assessment, the visual impact, possible confusion for a new customer.
Response time:	the time taken to respond, waiting, queuing
Point of Impact:	the first point of contact and initial impression
Delivery:	the actual events (MoTs?) of the service itself
Point of Departure:	any special events or opportunities when the customer leaves
Follow up:	obtaining feedback on satisfaction, or soliciting further business.

Further reading
G Lynn Shostack, "Designing Services that Deliver", *Harvard Business Review*, Vol 64, January / February 1984, pages 133-139
Vandermerwe, Sandra *The Eleventh Commandment*, Wiley, Chichester 1996, Chap 23
Mahesh, V.S. and Stanworth, James "Service Concept Delivery through System Design : The Case of Anglian Water Services", *Service Management : New perspectives, New initiatives*, C. Armistead and R. Teare (eds), Cassell, London, 1995
Robert Johnston, "A framework for delivering quality strategy in the customer processing operation", *Int Jnl of Quality and Reliability Mgmt*, 4, 4, 1987, pp 37-46

Data Display

Radar Charts
Also known as a web chart or a glyph chart, this type of chart is useful for the display of several performance indicators simultaneously. Deterioration in performance and relative speed of moving towards a goal are easily seen. Some companies display these charts prominently for all employees to see. In a radar chart, the target is at the centre, and the starting position shown near the circumference. Measures are plotted on lines joining the circumference to the centre : the closer to the centre, the better

To draw a radar chart :
1. Decide on the number of measures to be charted. Split these into two groups : those where more is better and those where less is better. These two types of measures are shown above and below the centreline. Further grouping may be desired; for instance, all quality measures together, and all people measures together.

2. Decide the targets, and the present positions of each of the measures. The target values should be shown at the centre. Choose a suitable scale for each measure, with the present situation shown some two-thirds along each line.

3. Arrange the spacing of the measure arms to be uniformly spread. (The angle between measures should be 180 degrees divided by the number of measures in each group + 1). Shade the one half of the diagram to indicate hat one group of measures is for more is better, the other less is better.

4. Plot the current status of the measures at regular intervals. Join the plots to form the web.

A sample chart is shown in the figure.

Box and Whisker Diagrams, Muli-Vari Charts, and Numbered Histograms
Variability is important in quality. To quote Ishikawa, "data without variability is false data". Deming agrees, claiming that most managers have very poor understanding of variation and make poor decisions as a result. So this section gives some practical easy ways to show variation.

Box and whisker diagrams are a clear way to show variation on a control chart. Say you have taken a sample of 20 readings. Arrange the readings in ascending order. The box shows the range of the middle 10 readings, and the whiskers show the range of all 20 readings. In other words, the box shows the limits of the first and third quartiles, and the whiskers the minimum and maximum values. Within the box, a line is drawn to indicate the median (i.e. the middle value in a set of readings arranged from lowest to highest). (Where the sample is large, the whiskers may show the extent of 97.5% of the readings, with individual readings beyond this range shown as dots.)

TECHNIQUES

Such diagrams are an instant way to appreciate the spread of data, particularly where the data is skewed (i.e. not evenly spread around the median value).

The multi-vari chart is a simplification of the box and whisker diagram, showing only the range (or lowest and highest values joined by a line). The average value is shown by a line crossing the vertical line.

DATA PRESENTATION

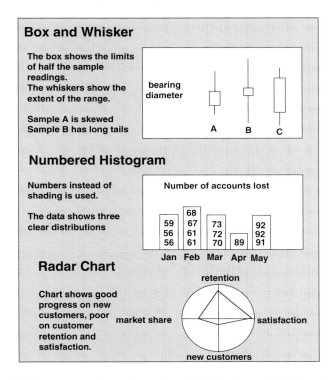

The numbered histogram uses the actual readings to fill in the bars of the histogram. In this way, a reader can get the actual numbers if she wishes or merely gain an overall impression from the bars.

Examples are shown in the figure.

Design of Experiments

Design of Experiments (DOE) is a family of techniques which enable a quality professional to home in rapidly on the most important variables in new product design or process improvement. DOE has a long history going back to Sir Ronald Fisher in 1930, but popularised and refined by Taguchi, Box, and more recently by Dorian Shainin.

Let us say that one suspects a number of variables (say temperature, pressure, metal thickness, length of time processed etc.) as having an influence on the quality level of a product. Traditionally these would be explored one variable at a time whilst maintaining all the other variables constant. Where there are several variables (say 13, each of which has 3 possible settings or "levels"), this becomes totally impractical (over 1.5 million trials would be needed) and is likely to miss the optimal combination especially if there are significant "interactions" between variables (eg. drink alone or drugs alone may be survivable, but in combination they could be fatal).

The DOE answer to this problem is to use an "Orthogonal Array" combined with Analysis of Variance (ANOVA: a straightforward statistical technique) to home in on the correct combinations. For the example given, only 27 trials would be necessary. This procedure was popularised by Taguchi who succeeded in taking it out of the realms of statistical specialisation to become a procedure that many engineers could use. Taguchi orthogonal tables are available in books such as by Peace.

A simple version of Taguchi works like this : Say you are investigating the flow of liquid through a membrane. The goal is to maximise the flow. First, identify the relevant factors; this may be done by brainstorming or experience. Say these are thickness, viscosity, and temperature. Each factor can have two "levels" (eg. thick/thin, low/high). Four trials would be necessary and the orthogonal array would be as shown in the figure. Notice that between any two columns each combination of levels occurs the same number of times. Undertake the trials, measuring flow each time. Analysis of variance is now used to calculate the percentage contribution of each factor. This identifies the critical factor(s) to watch. In some cases it is necessary to undertake further analysis to examine the interactions between factors.

There is no doubt that DOE is essential to achieving world class levels of quality in manufacturing such as the Six Sigma programme. For improvement, DOE is an order of magnitude more powerful than the basic 7 tools.

Despite considerable support, not all companies have achieved success through the Taguchi approach. It is still quite complex for the non statistician. More recently, Dorian Shainin has further refined and simplified DOE. His methods involve even more "engineering judgment" than those of Taguchi, and are not accepted by all purists. An additional problem is that the Shainin methods have in general not been written up to the extent of Taguchi, and are also subject to copyright. Nevertheless the Shainin techniques deserve considerably more attention than they have been given.

The Shainin approach to DOE uses a series of methods to home in on what is termed the "Red X" (i.e. the critical factor, or top problem) or the "Pink X" (a likely or important factor). The three basic methods are the "Multi-Vari Chart" (a more sophisticated form of run diagram; see under the 7 tools). "Components Search" (a four stage procedure used where there are interchangeable components, which involves identifying good and bad products, disassembling them and reassembling from components taken from good and bad products, then retesting), and "Paired Comparisons" (used when there are no components, which involves carefully observing and noting all differences between several pairs of products, one good and one bad in each pair, to give a strong clue as to the problem). Quite often these methods will reveal the Red X directly. If not, then having identified the Pink X's, one moves onto "Variables Search" and "Full Factorial" analysis. These are similar to the orthogonal array and ANOVA approach, but have been modified by Shainin.

Finally, the "B vs C" tool is a simple but effective method to determine if a better (or "B") process is truly better than a current (or "C") process, given a level of risk of being wrong. As an example, consider the case of 3 random samples taken from a current "C" process and 3 random samples taken from a possibly better "B" process. If the results are arranged in order from best to worst, and if the 3 best are all from the B process, then B stands a good chance of really being better. But if, for example, the two best readings are from B but the third best is from C, then there is a greater risk in concluding that B is really better. The "B vs C" tool extends this type of analysis to the case where there is known variation in the current process. (This is really a refinement of a well known statistical test for the difference between two means, but requiring far less data.) Such a test has wide application in quality management : from comparing two processes or methods, to comparing customer opinions about two products or services.

ORTHOGONAL ARRAYS

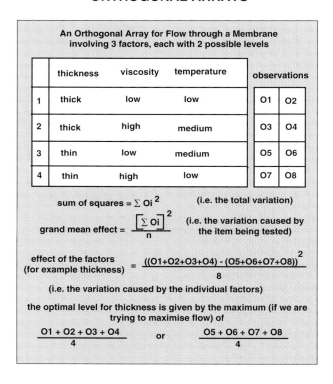

An Orthogonal Array for Flow through a Membrane involving 3 factors, each with 2 possible levels

	thickness	viscosity	temperature	observations	
1	thick	low	low	O1	O2
2	thick	high	medium	O3	O4
3	thin	low	medium	O5	O6
4	thin	high	low	O7	O8

sum of squares $= \Sigma \, Oi^2$ (i.e. the total variation)

$$\text{grand mean effect} = \frac{\left[\Sigma \, Oi\right]^2}{n}$$ (i.e. the variation caused by the item being tested)

$$\text{effect of the factors (for example thickness)} = \frac{((O1+O2+O3+O4) - (O5+O6+O7+O8))^2}{8}$$

(i.e. the variation caused by the individual factors)

the optimal level for thickness is given by the maximum (if we are trying to maximise flow) of

$$\frac{O1 + O2 + O3 + O4}{4} \quad \text{or} \quad \frac{O5 + O6 + O7 + O8}{4}$$

DOE fits in well with Quality Function Deployment (QFD). In QFD, a set of "technical specifications" (the columns in a QFD matrix) are set against the customer requirements (the rows in a QFD matrix). DOE is a powerful way to test which of the technical specifications has the most influence or is most sensitive.

Further Reading:
Keki R Bhote, *World Class Quality*, Amacom/ASQC, 1991. (Reviews traditional DOE and gives a full explanation of Shainin methods.)
Glen Stuart Peace, *Taguchi Methods : A Hands-On Approach*, Addison Wesley, 1993. A very comprehensive treatment of Taguchi.

T
E
C
H
N
I
Q
U
E
S

Failure Modes and Effect Analysis (FMEA)

Failure mode and effect analysis (FMEA) is a methodology to assess and reduce risk in systems, products or services. It aims to define, identify, prioritise, and eliminate known or potential failures at an early a stage as possible. FMEA is a Pareto type of analysis, homing in on the "vital few" failure modes. It is often used in conjunction with QFD (see separate section). As QFD is deployed from stage to stage, a corresponding FMEA is carried out. Other techniques used with FMEA include flowcharting, cause and effect diagrams, brainstorming / nominal group technique, process capability (Cpk) and design of experiments (see separate sections). The SERVQUAL dimensions are useful in service FMEA. With increasing risk of litigation in connection with products and services, several large companies (eg. Ford) require their suppliers to undertake FMEA analyses. But whether the aim is reduced risk from litigation or improved customer satisfaction, FMEA is becoming a standard procedure to be applied to all new products and services.

FMEA usually begins by assembling a group who are familiar with the product, service or system. If possible the group should include customers (internal or external), marketing and field service. The group will have the task of brainstorming out all the possible causes of failure. In addition to brainstorming, designers and engineers will be able to advise on likely modes of failure and records may show failures in past performance.

The four types of FMEA form a hierarchy, and can be used independently or in sequence. A **System FMEA** is used is used at the design stage to analyse overall systems including the interactions between functions so as to minimise failure effects. A **Design FMEA** is used to minimise design faults before they are passed to manufacturing. The **Process FMEA** focuses on failures caused in the manufacturing process. **Service FMEA** focuses on service failures. All four FMEAs use basically the same procedure and analysis sheet, an example of which is shown in the figure.

The fist stage is to obtain a sketch or engineering drawing of the system, product or service. Then a flowchart (process chart) of the product or service should be drawn up. Then, using the flowchart, step by step, all possible failure modes should be written down. The team should ask itself how could the process fail, and what might be found unacceptable or the customer. If warranty, field failure, or customer complaints data is available for a similar product or service this should be used. In a process or design FMEA the team should consider, for each step of the chart or component on the drawing, the inputs (parts, supply, testing), the process (manufacture), and outputs (inspection, transport, storage). In a service FMEA, the SERVQUAL dimensions of reliability, assurance, tangibles, empathy, responsiveness ("RATER") is a useful framework.

The effects of each mode of failure is then analysed under three criteria - severity, occurrence, and detection. (This is easy to remember: the mnemonic for the three criteria is SOD. FMEA tries to get to the root of the failure. Around roots are sods of earth.) For each mode of failure, the group allocates a score for each of the three. A 10 point scale is recommended. Severity indicates the seriousness of a failure, viewed from the perspective of the system or the customer. Occurrence is a rating reflecting the estimated number (or frequency) of failure. Detection reflects the possibility that a fault or problem will be discovered before it is released to the next stage (for system or design FMEAs) or to the final customer (manufacturing or service FMEAs). Like several other techniques much of the benefit of FMEA is derived from the discussions amongst group members as they assign relative scores. Thereafter the "RPN" or risk priority number is calculated by multiplying the three factors (S x O x D).

When all failure modes have been considered, the most critical or highest priority modes are identified by ranking the RPN scores. Clearly a high score indicates reasonable severity, more likely to occur, with reasonable difficulty of detection. Of course suitable actions must now be taken, in priority order. A threshold is usually established, above which action must be taken. For a 10 point scale the maximum RPN score is 1000 points, but the threshold may be as low as an RPN of 10 or 20.

FAILURE MODE and EFFECT ANALYSIS (FMEA)

Typical form used

Failures		Rankings			Risk Priority Number (RPN)
		Severity (A)	Occurrence (B)	Detection (C)	
potential mode of failure	potential causes and effects of failure	1 = none 3 = slight 5 = moderate 7 = major 9 = serious 10 = hazard	1 = never 3 = v slight 5 = low 7 = mod high 9 = v high 10 = almost certain	1 = certain 3 = high 5 = medium 7 = slight 9 = remote 10 = almost impossible	(A) * (B) * (C)

Note :
In addition there may be columns for existing conditions, suggested actions, implementation priority, implementation responsibility, and actions taken.

Once the threshold RPN number has been decided, the team should assess all modes of failure above the threshold for risk. If risk is small, no action is needed, but if high, action becomes essential.

Organizations using FMEA usually devise their own standard forms. An example is shown in the figure.

Further reading:
D.H. Stamatis, *Failure Mode and Effect Analysis*, ASQC Quality Press, Milwaukee, WI, 1995

The "Five Whys"

The 5 whys is a technique to ensure that the root causes of problems are sought out. It simply requires that the user asks "why?" several times over. The technique is called the "5 whys" because it is the experience of its inventor, the Toyota company, that "why" needs to be asked successively five times before the root cause is established.

This simple but very effective technique really amounts to a questioning attitude. Never accept the first reason given; always probe behind the answer. It goes along with the philosophy that a defect or problem is something precious; not to be wasted by merely solving it, but taking full benefit by exposing the underlying causes that have led to it in the first place. Many (for instance the MIT study on the worldwide car industry) believe that it is this unrelenting seeking out of root causes that have given the Japanese motor industry the edge on quality, reliability and productivity.

An example follows: A door does not appear to close as well as it should. Why? Because the alignment is not perfect. Why? Because the hinges are not always located in exactly the right place. Why? Because, although the robot that locates the hinge has high consistency, the frame onto which it is fixed is not always resting in exactly the same place. Why? Because the overall unit containing the frame is not stiff enough. Why? Because stiffness of the unit during manufacture does not appear to have been fully accounted for. So the real solution is to look at the redesign of the unit for manufacture.

Perhaps there are even more whys. Why did this happen in the first place? (Insufficient cooperation between design and manufacturing.) Why so? (It was a rushed priority.) Why? (Marketing had not given sufficient notice.) Why? And so on.

The 5 why analysis gives guidance to the role of an effective quality department. With total quality established, much responsibility for quality will be placed "at source", that is with the person that makes it. But this is not sufficient. The quality professionals need to be spending more time on the detective work of tracing problems to their root cause. This is real continuous improvement and prevention.

A variation of the 5 Why technique is the "5 How" technique. This is often used in tracing the cause of a failure in a product or in service delivery. ("How did that happen?"....) The thinking and procedure is exactly the same.

Force Field Analysis

The force field diagram is a simple but very effective tool to identify, in good time, what the various "pressures" for and against change are. A force field diagram is typically used early on in the implementation of quality programs such as SPC, may also be used for introducing change on a much smaller scale.

Force field diagrams were introduced by an organizational analyst, Kurt Lewin, in the 1920s. Their beauty lies in their simplicity which enable any employee to grasp and use the concept in minutes.

Consider a change, any change, that is being considered within the organization. In terms of quality this may be an attempt to reduce defects or improve service. The concept is simply that a chart is put up with a vertical line drawn on it. This represents the "status quo", or position at present. To the left of the line are listed the forces encouraging change to take place. To the right are the forces resisting the change. The pressures for change oppose the forces resisting change. Whether change will actually come about is dependent upon whether the forces for change will become dominant. To identify the forces at an early stage is half the battle - the forces for change can be effectively utilized and the forces opposing change effectively tackled. That's it!

An extension of the basic force field diagram is to show the linkages between the opposing forces. An example is shown in the figure. A further extension involves combination with the fishbone diagram.

FORCE FIELD ANALYSIS

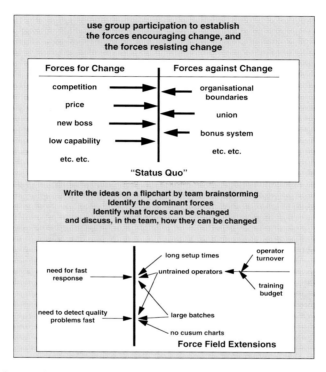

Force Field Extensions

The "trick" of using force field analysis is group participation and brainstorming. Not only does a group think of many factors which an individual would not, but the results become "their" analysis of the problem. Get the people concerned together and ask them, "Let's see, what are the factors that are tending to push us to make this change?" Enter them on the diagram. Then ask, "OK, now let's think about the factors that are preventing us from making this change." Enter them too. Now ask "What can be done about these factors?". In general there are two sets of answers encourage the "good' forces and reduce the "bad' forces. This should lead to a set of actions that the group has developed themselves, which can then be tackled.

In a service delivery case, where speed of delivery is the problem, the forces for change could include customer expectations. A more effective information system on delivery promises could reduce this pressure. Staff fears over redundancy may be opposing the change; perhaps guarantees have to be given.

Force field analysis can be used in conjunction with several other techniques and tools. A common one is the cause and effect (Ishikawa) diagram, which can be used to explore alternatives to the barriers that have been identified.

Hoshin

Hoshin (or Hoshin Kanri but also known as Jishu Kanri and in the West as Policy Deployment, and translated from the Japanese as a "methodology for setting strategic direction"), has become a well-accepted way of planning and communicating quality and productivity goals throughout an organisation. It is the emerging method of **strategic quality and productivity planning** and is used by leading Japanese companies (Toyota, Sony) and by leading Western companies (Hewlett Packard, Texas Instruments, Proctor and Gamble). Juran has pointed out that the concept follows closely the approach long used in managing company finance. It is, in essence, very simple but requires high levels of commitment and time. The objective is to communicate common objectives and gain commitment throughout the organisation.

A "Hoshin" is a word that is increasingly being heard in Western companies, to mean the breakthroughs or goals that are required to be achieved so as to meet the overall plan. Thus "what are your hoshins?" means what are the vital few things that you need to focus on. At the top level there may be only 3 to 5 hoshins. But at lower levels, the hoshins form a network or hierarchy of activities which lead to the top level hoshins. They are developed by consultation. Hoshin objectives are customer focused, based on company wide information, and measurable.

In essence, according to Juran, there are 5 stages :

* the business plan is expanded to include quality and productivity goals, not merely profitability and ROI.
* these goals are deployed down the organisation to determine the required resources, to agree on the actions, and to fix responsibilities
* appropriate measures are developed
* managers review progress regularly
* the reward system is adjusted to support the quality and productivity plan

Hoshin starts with the concept of homing in on the "vital few". Where there is little change in operating conditions, a company still needs to rely upon departmental management, but top management planning is not required. However, where there is significant change, top management must step in and steer the organisation. This requires strategic planning (for future alignment to identify the vital few strategic gaps), strategy management (for change), and cross functional management (to manage horizontal business processes). Hoshin is, however, not a planning tool but an execution tool. It deploys the "voice of the customer", not just the profit goals.

Departmental management should be relied upon for "kaizen" (i.e. incremental) improvements, but breakthrough improvements which often involve cross functional activities and top level support, should be the focus for hoshin planning. (We can note here similarities with related fields - Juran talks about the need for project by project improvement to achieve breakthroughs which attack chronic wastes, in BPR Davenport talks about "sequential alteration" between continuous improvement and process reengineering, and in *Lean Thinking* Womack and Jones discuss kaizen and kaikaku.)

Once the vital few strategic gaps have been identified by top management, employees and teams at each level are required to develop plans as to how to close the gaps. This requires that employees have access to adequate up-to-date information - breaking down "confidentiality" barriers found in many Western organisations. There must be a clear link, or cause and effect relationship, between the organisational goals, key objectives, and activities. Measures, including check points, are developed by the employees themselves. At each level, Deming's Plan, Do, Check, Adjust cycle operates. And, there is strong use of both the "7 tools" and the New Tools (see separate sections) to analyse, quantify, and control. Further, root cause analysis, using the 5 Whys method (see separate section), is used at each level.

TECHNIQUES

The Hoshin concept can be seen as two stages : Planning for Focus and Planning for Achievement. In the Focus stage, thinking about the 3 to 5 year plan leads to identification of critical success factors and the "vital few" upon which to concentrate. Then in the Achievement stage, breakthrough goals are developed for the vital few areas, which are expanded out into annual targets, which in turn lead to the necessary projects and actions. Top management should be concerned with developing the "vision". But, unlike many western companies, this vision is translated into required actions. One way is to use "backward planning" - starting with the ideal design and working backwards, year by year, to identify the constraints that need to be eliminated.

Hoshin uses the "outcome, what, how, how much, and who" framework. At Board level, a visioning process covers the key questions of what is to be the required outcome for the company (eg 10% growth), what is to be achieved (eg reductions in lead time), how is it to be done (eg extend lean manufacturing principles), and how much (all shops to be on JIT by year end). Specific quality and productivity goals are established. Then, the "who" are discussed. Normally there will be several managers responsible for achieving these objectives. Appropriate measures are also developed.

The objective cascading process of Hoshin is also different to most traditional models. In traditional models, cascading plans come down from the top without consultation, and there is little vertical and especially horizontal alignment. In Hoshin, people who must implement the plan design the plan. The means, not just the outcomes, must be specified. And there are specific and ongoing checks to see that local plans add up to overall plans.

At each level a group meeting takes place. This is referred to as "Catch Ball" (ideas are tossed around like a ball) or "Huddles". Ideas flow from all directions, and agreement is arrived at by consensus and negotiation, not authority. If a goal is really infeasible the upper tier is informed. (See similarities with Open Book Management). A Japanese word for this is the "Ringi" system.

Feedback goes in the reverse direction. Difficulties and constraints are identified and fed back to the level above who are required to act accordingly. Also, measures are taken and gaps identified. If a problem is identified, corrective action is taken in relation to the process, not the person. This "blame free" culture is critical.

A final stage in the cycle is the Hoshin Audit where achievements against plan are formally rolled up the organisation. Exceptions are noted and carried forward. Hewlett Packard does this very formally once per quarter, "flagging up" (by yellow or red "flag") problem areas. Intel uses, against each Hoshin, a classification showing highlights, lowlights, issues, and plans. Again, root causes are identified.

Hoshin is in essence an expanded form of "team briefing" but requires written commitment, identification of goals, the setting of measures, and discussion at each level. In Western companies, top management sometimes spends much time on corporate vision but then fails to put in place a mechanism to translate the vision into deliverables and measures, at each level in the organisation. Hoshin may go some way to explaining why in Japanese companies the decision making process is slower, but implementation is much faster and smoother.

Further reading:

Y. Akao, *Hoshin Kanri : Policy Deployment for Successful TQM*, Productivity Press, Portland, 1991
Michele L Bechtell, *The Management Compass : Steering the Corporation Using Hoshin Planning*, AMA Management Briefing, New York, 1995

The Importance Performance Matrix (and PGCV Index)

When measuring performance or collecting survey information on service quality, it is important that a two-dimensional view be taken: Performance along one axis and importance along the other. This was (probably) first suggested by Kotler in 1987, has appeared in several quality-related publications since then, with the latest variant by Slack et al. Collecting information along these two dimensions greatly improves the utility of the information. Thus a high score on performance may mean "overkill" or "achieving target", and a low score on performance may indicate urgent action or simply low priority. Often quality or customer satisfaction surveys reflect only the dimension of satisfaction or performance but ignore the importance to the customer of the factor being surveyed. This can lead to misleading conclusions. It's a simple but powerful idea.

SATISFACTION - IMPORTANCE MATRIX

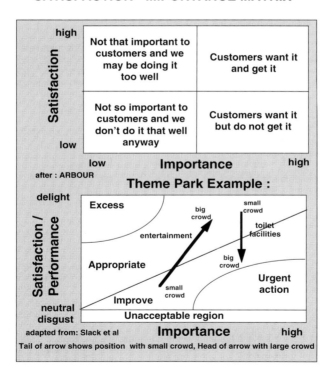

In a customer survey, using for instance a 1 to 5 rating scale, there should always be two scales for each question : one going from excellent to poor (or performed well to performed badly) to cover satisfaction or performance, and the other from important to not important. Then, when plotted on a matrix, the priority clusters become clear. See the figure.

A further dimension is also possible : one could collect the performance importance data by category or market segment and show the variation on a performance importance matrix. For instance, one could categorise performance importance information at a theme park by the number of attendees and discover that some aspects might migrate from the high-low (overkill) quadrant to the low-high (priority) quadrant as the crowd size grows and facilities get pressed for capacity. See the lower figure.

The potential gain in customer value (PGCV) index is an alternative way to quantify the information. The index is made up as follows :

$$PGCV = UDCV - ACV$$

where
UDCV (ultimately desired customer value) = $I \times P_{max}$
ACV (achieved customer value) = $I \times P_{achieved}$
and
I is the importance rating by the surveyed customer
P_{max} is the maximum score for performance (i.e. top of the scale)
$P_{achieved}$ is the performance score actually achieved.

The higher the PGCV score the greater the gap or shortfall in customer expectations. PGCV scores are best used to compare several aspects or dimensions of quality (see for instance the SERVQUAL dimensions). Ranking PGCV scores in descending order gives management a good idea on priorities. The PGCV score can also be used for further statistical analysis, for example to test the significance of various dimensions.

Further reading:
Willard C Hom, "Making Customer Service Analysis a Little Easier with the PGCV Index", *Quality Progress*, Vol 30, No 3, March 1997, pages 89-93
Philip Kotler, *Marketing for Non-profit Organizations*, Prentice Hall, Englewood Cliffs, 1987, pages 635-636
Slack, N., Chambers, Harland, Harrison, Johnston, *Operations Management*, Pitman, London, 1995, page 740.

Kaizen

Kaizen is the Japanese name for continuous improvement. As such it is a vital part of total quality. It brings together several of the tools and techniques described in this book plus a few besides. The word Kaizen was made popular in the West by Maasaki Imai who wrote a book of the same name. Although a registered name of the Kaizen Institute, the word is now widely used and understood and has appeared in the English dictionary.

According to Imai, Kaizen comprises several elements. Kaizen is both a philosophy and a set of tools.

The Philosophy of Kaizen: Quality begins with the customer. But customers views are continuously changing and standards are rising, so continuous improvement is required. Kaizen is dedicated to continuous improvement, in small increments, at all levels, forever (!). Everyone has a role, from top management to shop floor employees. Top management must allocate the resources and establish the strategy, systems, procedures and organisational structures necessary for Kaizen to work. Middle managers are responsible for implementing Kaizen. They must monitor performance of the continuous improvement programme, and ensure that employees are educated in the use of the necessary tools. Supervisors are responsible for applying Kaizen. They must maintain the rate of suggestions, coach, and improve communications at the workplace. And shop-floor employees must make suggestions, learn new jobs, use the tools, and generally participate in continuous improvement activities individually and in teams. Imai's book has several examples of how this philosophy is works its way down the organisational hierarchy in Japanese companies.

Imai believes that without active attention, the gains made will simply deteriorate (like the engineers concept of entropy). But Imai goes further. Unlike Juran who emphasises "holding the gains", Kaizen involves building on the gains by continuing experimentation and innovation.

According to Imai there are several guiding principles. These include : Questioning the rules (standards are necessary but work rules are there to be broken and must be broken with time), Developing resourcefulness (it is a management priority to develop the resourcefulness and participation of everyone), Get to the Root Cause (don't solve problems superficially), Eliminate the whole task (question whether a task is necessary; in this respect Kaizen is similar to BPR), Reduce or change activities (be aware of opportunities to combine tasks).

The Tools of Kaizen: Kaizen incorporates several tools but the most well known are the Deming Cycle, "5 S", the "5 M Checklist", and the 5 Whys. Also central to Kaizen is the recognition and elimination of waste or Muda (see the section on the Wastes). 5 S and the 5 Whys are described in a separate sections. Visual management is a feature ; making operations and quality visible through charts, displayed schedules, kanban, painted designated inventory and tool locations, and the like. A brief description of 5M follows:

The 5 M Checklist is intended to ensure that all 5 of men (people), machine, material, method, and measurement is considered in any process improvement or problem solution. The 5 M's are often incorporated in constructing Cause and Effect Diagrams as the basic fishbone framework. (Cause and Effect Diagrams are one of the 7 Tools).

Recently, Imai has extended and elaborated on Kaizen in Gemba Kaizen. "Gemba" is the workplace. But this Japanese word has taken on a significance far beyond its literal translation. Taiichi Ohno, legendary Toyota engineer and father of the JIT system, said that "Management begins at the workplace". This whole philosophy can best be captured by the single word: Gemba. Of course, Gemba is by no means confined to the factory.

Under Gemba, if your organisation has a problem or a decision, go to Gemba first. Do not attempt to resolve problems away from the place of action. Do not let operators come to the manager, let the manager go to the workplace. Spend time on the factory floor or at the service counter. This is the basis of so much Japanese management practice : that new Honda management recruits should spend time working in assembly and in stores, that marketeers from Nikon should spend time working in camera shops, that Toyota sends its Lexus design team to live in California for three months, and so on. Imai's latest book includes examples of Kaizen applied in both manufacturing and service.

Further reading
Maasaki Imai, *Kaizen : The Key to Japan's Competitive Success*, McGraw Hill, New York, 1986
Maasaki Imai, *Gemba Kaizen*, McGraw Hill, New York, 1997

TECHNIQUES

Market Surveys and Customer Observation

All organisations require information about customer needs, expectations, and satisfaction, so market research and surveys are vital. There are several types of market or customer survey but the real issue is to select the right mix and to make sure that information collected is used effectively. For instance, Hewlett Packard uses three linked approaches: A Customer Satisfaction Survey, a Customer Feedback System, and Customer Visits which are carefully integrated for comprehensiveness and efficiency.

But first, consideration needs to be given to which customers should be surveyed. This is not obvious, and depends on the questions you want answered. Candidates are current customers (by spending category, location, need ?), past customers, potential customers, competitor's customers, or customer's customer.

Here we consider the major types of survey:

Focus Groups : A small group of customers or potential customers gathered to discuss open-ended questions. Powerful, and can lead down unexpected roads. Requires a skilled facilitator, and many not be representative of customer base, unless particular care is taken. Group members may stimulate each other, to produce further ideas.

Questionnaires : Answers to specific questions are sought. Inexpensive. Low response rate common, requires skilled questionnaire and sample design to be effective and representative. Temptingly easy, but to be meaningful should be first tested on a representative group, validated and statistically justified. Deming and Juran both emphasised that quality is in the eyes of the customer. Therefore a good satisfaction questionnaire should be a two stage process : the first a pilot to determine what it is that are important to customers, and the second to survey opinion. (See also the section on The Performance Importance Matrix).

Interviews : One-on-one talk seeking insights as to why a customer has or has not purchased, or has "defected"; best done close after the event (a new customer, or with a customer where new business has failed to be gained or has been lost). Requires active follow up, skill with defecting customers, and assurance of confidentiality.

Mystery Shopping : A false or posed customer goes through the whole process with your company and with competitors. Not confined to shopping but can be used in any service. Valuable first hand documentation, but possibility of being accused of spying or mistrust.

Customer visits : To check on-site (for example, at a customer's home) on satisfaction levels, and on where and how a product is being used. Questioning users on-site may be very insightful, and may lead to unexpected opportunity. Requires customer goodwill, but is often appreciated by customers.

Debriefing of employees : Surveys show that perhaps three times as many complaints are registered with frontline staff as are received in writing. In many organisations, the views of customers picked up by front-line staff are simply lost. Debriefing must be done in a relaxed, supportive, no-blame atmosphere. Employees may also have good ideas as to new products or services.

Telephone surveys : See questionnaires. May get higher response than mail, but run a risk of greater annoyance.

Freephone (Toll free / Hot line) : Making complaining easier. Effective because some problems can be solved immediately, or you are speaking to customers at the time they are actually experiencing problems. This is not the case with questionnaires, for example, and customers are prone to forgetting detail.

Customer Tours : Customers invited to visit the factory, service facility, bridge of ship or aeroplane. Can create goodwill with high-ticket items and can use the opportunity to discuss reasons for purchase, needs and expectations with captive customers. Confidence and loyalty building.

The Internet : A new source of customer satisfaction data is the internet. These have the advantage of being frank, uncensored, "from the hip" remarks and experiences. Some include photographs of products that have gone wrong - a well known 4WD vehicle is a case in point. Discussions and evaluations of consumer products and services appear in activity and hobby oriented web pages, and useful information can be obtained from newsgroups. Moreover, newsgroups can be continually monitored, automatically. You will need a search engine such as Alta Vista or, for newsgroups, Deja News (on http://www.dejanews.com)

Observation :
Observation has emerged as a most powerful way of creating innovative products and services, and is therefore particularly relevant for Kano "performance" and "Delighter" factors. (See the section on the Kano model). Observation can also be combined with some of the previous survey methods, for instance during focus groups, mystery shopping, or customer tours. The method involves close observation, with or without video. Variations are a hidden camera, one-way mirrors, and sound recording.

Opportunities and situations where observation is useful include : Frustration (with a new product ?), wasted time (in queues, with forms, at arrival, having to search for information?), anxiety (whilst waiting for answers ?), doing things wrong or dangerously (as a result of unclear instructions; accidentally touching or using ?), unexpected or unintended use (situations where it was not envisaged for the product or service to be used), product modification (washing jeans to give a worn look; installing "extras"), and commonly used partner products or services (an instruction book with new software; snacks at a filling station.)

Further reading:
Terry G Vavra, *Improving Your Measurement of Customer Satisfaction*, ASQC Quality Press, Milwaukee, WI,1997
Byron J Finch, "A New Way to Listen to the Customer", *Quality Progress*, May 1997, pp 73-76

Moments of Truth (MoT)

Moments of truth (MoT) is a concept rather than a technique, apparently first articulated by Jan Carlzon, the head of the Scandinavian airline SAS. It is a powerful concept for quality management, and so deserves a place in any gallery of quality concepts. The concept was made even more popular by Albrect and Zemke in their book "Service America!"

A moment of truth is that moment in time when a customer comes into contact with the products, systems, people, or procedures of a organization and as a result leads the customer to make a judgement about the quality of that organizations' products or services.

It is clear that scores, even hundreds, of MoTs are possible for a single customer in interaction with a company. Each one is a potential point of dissatisfaction where, as a result, the customer may be lost, or conversely where the customer can experience "delight" and become a loyal user. Some MoTs are critical other less so, and here it is useful to bring in the Kano model concepts (see seperate section). Moreover, the customer builds an impression of the organisation through the cumulative effect of MoT experiences. In many services (eg hotels, holidays, travel, parcel

TECHNIQUES

delivery, banking, consultancy) the customer has little or no tangible product that remains after the operation is complete. All that the customer is left with is a memory - of hundreds of moments of truth. That is why the proactive analysis of MoTs should be an important concern of management, particularly if they believe that it costs five times as much to regain a lost customer as it does to acquire a new one.

This leads to MoT analysis where the points of potential dissatisfaction can be proactively identified. MoT analysis begins with the assembly of process-type diagrams (these are referred to as "cycles of service"; see seperate section). Every minute step taken by a customer in his or her dealings with company products, services or people is recorded. This begins when the customer first makes contact (perhaps by telephone, mail, or in person) to the last time the product or service is experienced. There would be a different chart for each type of customer service. Whether called a process chart or a cycle of service, the point is that the steps follow the experiences of the customer, irrespective of organizational boundaries or departments.

The problem from a quality management viewpoint is that most MoTs take place away from the eyes of management, but in interaction with the "front line" staff. All MoTs occur with either the visible product or with the front line - with the latter by far the predominant case in the case of service industry. That is why it is desirable to work through all possible MoTs in advance. It is said that, even if a product or service fails, if the backup service is good the customer will not be resentful and may even be grateful. One may argue that it is not possible to identify all MoTs, but at least if a systematic effort has been made the number and severity of unexpected failures will be minimized. In this respect MoT analysis has much in common with failure mode and effect analysis (FMEA).

Pareto analysis (see the 7 tools), is also relevant to MoT. The "vital few" MoTs are the critical ones to be managed well. And value analysis may also be a useful technique in conjunction with MoT. VA enables one to identify the critical functions (MoT expressed in verb and noun format), and to use creative thinking in their improvement.

Further reading:
Jan Carlzon, *Moments of Truth*, Harper and Row, 1987
Christian Grönroos, *Service Management and Marketing : Managing the Moments of Truth in Service Competition,* Lexinngton Books, MA, 1990

The Nominal Group Technique (NGT)

The nominal group technique (NGT) is a particular form of team brainstorming and creative problem identification. It is worth specific mention since it is now widely used in place of "classic" brainstorming. NGT is a well researched procedure that draws on both individual and group strengths, using each as appropriate, and which prevents domination by particular individuals. It is a technique that supplements most of the other techniques discussed, and can be used for issue identification, idea generation, and problem solving. NGT has been widely used in quality and productivity improvement and in organizational strategy formulation.

A team is the basic requirement; preferably a multi-level, multi-discipline team. Different disciplines bring different perspectives, and different levels cross the communication boundaries that exist in every organization. A team of between 8 and 12 is considered ideal and there is also a facilitator and perhaps an assistant. The facilitator usually explains to the team how NGT works before the actual process begins.

NGT begins with the facilitator reading out a **statement of the problem** to be tackled by the team. The statement must be carefully prepared and written out, not merely presented "off the cuff". After hearing the statement there are likely to be questions seeking clarification. The facilitator should not now try to revise the problem statement but should encourage the participants to restate the problem in their own words. The facilitator may even nominate two or three members to restate the problem. This is a deliberate stage which forces the team to think through the problem statement in their own words. The facilitator must prevent any team member from dominating, and must not allow the problem to be "hijacked". The original problem statement written out by the facilitator is not altered, it is merely a process of restating in the team's own terms. The facilitator allows discussion to continue until problem formulation, as expressed by the team, seems satisfactory.

The next stage is called **silent generation.** About 15 minutes is allowed for this, during which time silence is required. Each team member is asked to write out his or her responses, alternatives, or suggestions to the problem statement. The team should remain in one room for this purpose since the "atmosphere" of work encourages mental concentration. Team members who may finish early are still required to remain in the room without talking. The silent generation period is used because study has shown that this is the most effective initial way to generate a variety of viewpoints and ideas. The facilitator will discourage talking but may cut short the period if all seem to have completed the task. The facilitator would bring the period to an end, but emphasize that creativity has not stopped and that new ideas can be added to the team member's lists at any time.

NOMINAL GROUP TECHNIQUE

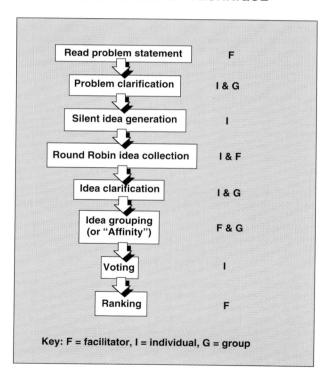

Stage	Key
Read problem statement	F
Problem clarification	I & G
Silent idea generation	I
Round Robin idea collection	I & F
Idea clarification	I & G
Idea grouping (or "Affinity")	F & G
Voting	I
Ranking	F

Key: F = facilitator, I = individual, G = group

Now the **"round robin"** stage begins. Each team member is asked in turn to put forward an idea or suggestion. These will usually be taken from team member's lists but not necessarily so. Often, additional ideas will be stimulated by the ideas of others. When each idea is put forward, the facilitator may seek clarification from the team member, but must not change or develop the idea. Other team members are not allowed to participate in these discussions but must wait their turn. No criticism is allowed by team members or the facilitator. As each idea is put forward and clarified it is entered onto a chart by the facilitator or assistant. Only one idea is put forward by each team member before passing onto the next member. Round robin continues until ideas begin to run out and team members "pass". When there are no more ideas the stage ends.

With all ideas entered onto charts displayed around the room, the next stage begins. This is called **clarification.** The stage allows the power of group creativity to take over. The facilitator goes through each suggestion in turn. Once again criticism is not allowed, and each idea is further explained as necessary. Team members may suggest modifications or additions. The team must also group ideas that they consider to be similar. This may result in some deletions and rephrasing. It is important that this stage does not get bogged down in detail, so the facilitator must cut short any rambling discussion. (Note: although not part of the original NGT theory, this is the stage at which various creative thinking concepts, such as the de Bono "po" word can be introduced as an addition.)

The next stage is **selection and ranking.** Cards are now issued to all team members and, once again individually and in silence, each member is asked to select the top (say) six ideas. Each member writes the ideas on cards together with the ranking at the top of the card. (Actually a reverse ranking with 6 points for the best and 1 for the last). Often, team members are asked to proceed in two sub-stages. The first involves selecting the top six ideas and writing these onto the cards. The second proceeds as follows: first the top idea of the six is selected and a 6 entered on the card. Then the worst of the six is selected and a 1 entered. Then the second best is selected and a 5 entered, and the second worst gets a 2, and so on.

The next stage involves the **final ranking.** This is done by the facilitator and assistant who gather the cards and write up the results on a new chart. Next to each idea, transferred from the cards, is written the rankings as given by all the team members. Each idea will have a string of numbers, being the rankings as given by team members. (There may be several zeros, where a team member did not rank the idea in the top six.) Now the scores are added up to give the final ranking. In the case of a tie, the idea having the highest number of team member rankings, as opposed to the total score, wins.

The result is a ranked set of ideas which, even though there may not be complete team consensus, at least come close to this ideal and have been generated without dominance by any team member.

Precontrol

Statistical Process Control (SPC) is more suited to longer production runs where a large number of samples can be taken over time. Unfortunately this is not the case with many JIT systems. Also, particularly with JIT, it is important to verify as quickly as possible if a changeover has been undertaken correctly and the process is capable of producing good quality parts. One possibility is to use Precontrol, originally developed by consultants Rath and Strong.

The procedure is as follows :

1   Divide the tolerance (or specification) band (i.e. the area between the upper and lower tolerance limits) into 4 equal bands. The middle two bands are the green zone (and should be coloured green on a chart). The two outer areas are called the yellow zone. Beyond the tolerance limits is the red band.

2   Following Changeover (to check capability) : Measure 5 consecutive units.
If all five are in the green zone, the process is in control. Production can start.
If even one is in the red zone, the process is not in control. Production must not start.
Reset the process.
If one is in the yellow zone, a 'special cause' may be present. Take another sample of
5. Better still, investigate.
If two consecutive readings fall in the yellow zone, adjust the process and restart the
measurement process.

3   During production : Take samples of two consecutive units.
If even one unit falls in the red zone, stop production and investigate. Return to Step 2.
If both units fall in the yellow zones, stop production and investigate. Return to Step 2.
If one unit falls in the yellow zone and one in the green, continue.
If both units fall in the green, continue.

4   Sample 6 pairs between setups. (e.g. for an hourlong batch, sample approximately
every 10 minutes)

PRECONTROL CHARTS

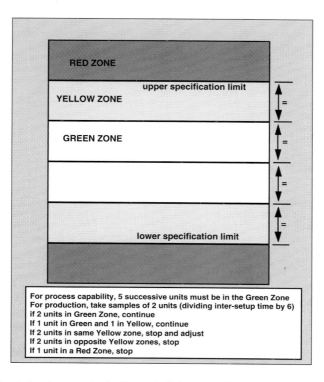

RED ZONE

upper specification limit

YELLOW ZONE

GREEN ZONE

lower specification limit

For process capability, 5 successive units must be in the Green Zone
For production, take samples of 2 units (dividing inter-setup time by 6)
if 2 units in Green Zone, continue
If 1 unit in Green and 1 in Yellow, continue
If 2 units in same Yellow zone, stop and adjust
If 2 units in opposite Yellow zones, stop
If 1 unit in a Red Zone, stop

TECHNIQUES

The method is obviously very simple. Precontrol charts can be printed ahead of time and no
statistical training is necessary. Implementation is immediate. However, critics have pointed out
that Precontrol is based on tolerance limits, not on process variation as is the case with SPC. As

such the method relies on these tolerances being carefully set during design. Some statisticians have pointed out that a sample size of 2 may simply be inadequate. Nevertheless, the technique is statistically based and is likely to be reliable under many circumstances. Bhote has been a strong advocate of Precontrol, has pointed out some weaknesses in SPC, and claims that SPC is a "horse and buggy" in the Jet Age. Bhote claims that Precontrol has overtaken SPC in popularity in Japan.

References:
Dorian and Peter Shainin, "Precontrol versus X and R Charting", *Quality Engineering,* Vol 1 No 4, 1989.
Keki R Bhote, *World Class Quality*, AMACOM/ASQC, 1991, Chapter 15.

Quality Function Deployment (QFD)

Quality Function Deployment is a "meta" technique that has gown hugely in importance over the last decade and is now used in both product and service design. It is a meta technique because many other techniques described in this book can or should be used in undertaking QFD design or analysis. These other techniques include several of the "new tools", benchmarking, market surveys, the Kano model, the performance - importance matrix, and FMEA.

Customer needs are identified and systematically compared with the technical or operating characteristics of the product or service. The process brings out the relative importance of customer needs which, when set against the characteristics of the product leads to the identification of the most important or sensitive characteristics. These are the characteristics which need development or attention. Although the word "product" is used in the descriptions which follow, QFD is equally applicable in services. Technical characteristics then become the service characteristics.

Perhaps a chief advantage of QFD is that it is carried out by a multi-disciplinary team all concerned with the particular product. QFD acts as a forum for marketing, design, engineering, manufacturing, distribution and others to work together using a concurrent or simultaneous engineering approach. QFD is then the vehicle for these specialists to attack a problem together rather than by "throwing the design over the wall" to the next stage. QFD is therefore not only concerned with quality but with the simultaneous objectives of reducing overall development time, meeting customer requirements, reducing cost, and producing a product or service which fits together and works well the first time. The mechanics of QFD are not cast in stone, and can easily be adapted to local innovation.

The first QFD matrix is also referred to as the "house of quality". This is because of the way the matrices in QFD fit together to form a house-shaped diagram. A full QFD exercise may deploy several matrix diagrams, forming a sequence which gradually translates customer requirements into specific manufacturing steps and detailed manufacturing process requirements. For instance, a complete new car could be considered at the top level but subsequent exercises may be concerned with the engine, body shell, doors, instrumentation, brakes, and so on. Thereafter the detail would be deployed into manufacturing and production. But the most basic QFD exercise would use only one matrix diagram which seeks to take customer requirements and to translate them into specific technical requirements.

The "House of Quality" Diagram
In the sections opposite the essential composition of the basic house of quality diagram is explained. Refer to the figure.

Customer requirements

The usual starting point for QFD is the identification of customer needs and benefits. This is also referred to as "the voice of the customer" or "the whats". Customers may be present or future, internal or external, primary or secondary. All the conventional tools of marketing research are relevant, as well as techniques such as complaint analysis and focus groups. Customers may include owners, users, and maintainers, all of whom have separate requirements. Refer to the section on market research. After collection comes the problem of how to assemble the information before entering it into the rows. In this the "new tools" of affinity and tree diagrams have been found to be especially useful. This results in a hierarchy; on the primary level are the broad customer requirements, with the secondary requirements adding the detail.

QUALITY FUNCTION DEPLOYMENT (QFD)

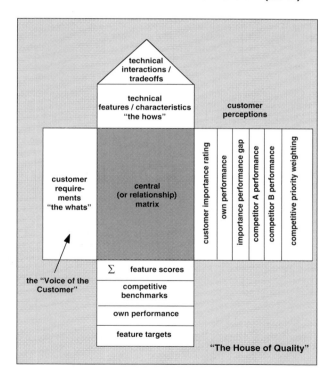

Marketing would have responsibility for assembling much of the customer information, but the team puts it together. Marketing may begin by circulating the results of surveys and by a briefing. It is important to preserve the "voice of the customer", but the team may group like requirements using the affinity diagram. The team must not try to "second guess" or to assume that they know best what is needed by customers.

Rankings or relative importance of customer requirements

When the customer requirements are assembled onto the matrix on the left of the house diagram, weightings are added on the right to indicate the importance of each requirement. Weightings are established by market research or focus groups or, failing these, the team may determine rankings by a technique such as "pairwise comparison". (In pairwise comparison, each requirement is compared with each other. The most important of the two requirements gains a point, and all scores are added up to determine final rankings.) The Kano model (see separate section) is very often used with QFD as an aid in determining appropriate weightings.

Technical characteristics and associated rankings

Customer requirements and weightings are displayed in rows. The technical characteristics (or "hows" or "technical responses") form the columns. These characteristics are the features that the organisation provides in the design to respond to the customer requirements (For a kettle this may include power used, strength of the materials, insulation, sealing, materials used, and noise.) Once again these could be assembled into groups to form a hierarchy, using the Tree Diagram. Here the team will rely on its own internal expertise. There are at least two ways to develop technical characteristics. On way is go via measures that respond to customer needs. For instance a customer need for the kettle may be "quick boil". The measure is "minutes to boil" and the technical response is the power of the heating element. Another is to go directly to functions, based on the teams experience or on current technology.

The Planning Matrix

To the right of the central matrix is found the planning matrix. This is a series of columns which evaluate the importance, satisfaction, and goal for each customer need. (See the figure). The first column shows importance to the customer of each need. Here a group of customers may be asked to evaluate the importance of each need on a 1 to 5 scale (1=not important, 5=vital, of highest importance). In the next column the current performance of each product or service need, is rated by the group of customers. The difference between the columns is the gap - a negative number indicates possible overprovision, a positive number indicates a shortfall. The reader will recognise that here the QFD process is duplicating the importance-performance matrix (see separate section), or the SERVQUAL gaps. The next few columns give the competitors current performance on each customer need. The aim of this part of the exercise is to clearly identify the "SWOT" (strengths, weaknesses, opportunities, threats) of competitor products as against your own. For example, the kettle manufacturer may be well known for product sturdiness, but be weak on economy. If economy is highly ranked, this will point out an opportunity and, through the central matrix, show what technical characteristics can be used to make up this deficiency. The gap (if any) between own and competitors performance can then be determined. Since the QFD team now has detail on the gap for each need and of the importance of each need, they can then decide the desired goal for each customer need - normally expressed in the same units as the performance column. Deciding the goal for each need is an important task for the QFD team. These goals are the weights to be used in the relationship matrix. (Note : in some versions of QFD there are additional columns).

The Central (or Relationship) Matrix

The central matrix lies at the heart of the house of quality diagram. This is where customer needs are matched against each technical characteristic. The nature of the relationship is noted in the matrix by an appropriate symbol. The team can devise their own symbols; for instance, numbers may indicate the relative strength of the relationship or simply ticks may suffice. The strength of the relationship or impact is recorded in the matrix. These relationships may be nil, possibly linked, moderately linked or strongly linked. Corresponding weights (typically 0, 1, 3, 9) are assigned . Thereafter the scores for each technical characteristic are determined as in the "new tool" of Matrix Analysis (refer to the section in this book which details how a total score is determined for each characteristic). This matching exercise is carried out by the team based on their experience and judgement. The idea is to clearly identify all means by which the "whats" can be achieved by the "hows". It will also check if all "whats" can in fact be achieved (insufficient technical characteristics?), and if some technical characteristics are not apparently doing anything (redundancy?). A blank row indicates a customer requirement not met. A blank column indicates a redundant technical feature. In practice, matrix evaluation can be a very large task (a moderate size QFD matrix of 30 x 30 has 900 cells to be evaluated). The team may split the task between them.

Technical Matrix

Immediately below the relationship matrix appears one or more rows for rankings such as cost or technical difficulty or development time. The choice of these is dependent on the product. These will enable the team to judge the efficacy of various technical solutions. The prime row uses the customer weightings and central matrix to derive the relative technical characteristic rankings. A full example is given under Matrix Analysis in the New Tools section of this booklet.

Next below the relationship matrix comes one or more rows for competitive evaluation. Here, where possible, "hard" data is used to compare the actual physical or engineering characteristics of your product against those of competitors. In the kettle example these would include watts of electricity, mass, and thermal conductivity of the kettle walls. This is where benchmarking is done. By now the QFD team will know the critical technical characteristics, and these should be benchmarked against competitors (See the section on Benchmarking - especially competitive benchmarking). So to the right of the relationship matrix one can judge relative customer perceptions and below the relative technical performance.

The bottom row of the house, which is also the "bottom line" of the QFD process, are the target technical characteristics. These are expressed in physical terms and are decided upon after team discussion of the complete house contents, as described below. The target characteristics are, for some, the final output of the exercise, but many would agree that it is the whole process of information assembly, ranking, and team discussion that goes into QFD which is the real benefit, so that the real output is improved inter-functional understanding.

The roof of the house

The roof of the house is the technical interaction matrix. The diagonal format allows each technical characteristic to be viewed against each other one. This simply reflects any technical trade-offs that may exist. For example with the kettle two technical characteristics may be insulation ability and water capacity. These have a negative relationship; increasing the insulation decreases the capacity. These interactions are made explicit, using the technical knowledge and experience of the team. Some cells may highlight challenging technical issues - for instance thin insulation in a kettle, which may be the subject of R&D work leading to competitive advantage. The roof is therefore useful to highlight areas in which R&D work could best be focused.

Using the house as a decision tool

The central matrix shows what the required technical characteristics are that will need design attention. The costs of these can be seen with reference to the base rows. This may have the effect of shifting priorities if costs are important. Then the technical trade-offs are examined. Often there will be more than one technical way to impact a particular customer requirement, and this is clear from rows in the matrix. And it may also be that one technical alternative has a negative influence on another customer requirement. This is found out by using the roof matrix. Eventually, through a process of team discussion, a team consensus will emerge. This may take some time, but experience shows that time and cost is repaid many times over as the actual design, engineering and manufacturing steps proceed.

The bottom line is now the target values of technical characteristics. This set can now go into the next house diagram. This time the target technical characteristics become the "customer requirements" or "whats", and the new vertical columns (or "hows") are, perhaps, the technologies, the assemblies, the materials, or the layouts. And so the process "deploys" until the team feels that sufficient detail has been considered to cover all coordination considerations in the process of bringing the product to market.

Note: QFD may be used in several stages in order to "deploy" customer requirements all the way to the final manufacturing or procedural stages. Here the outcome of one QFD matrix (e.g. the technical specifications), becomes the input into the next matrix which may aim to look at process specifications to make the product.

Assembling the team

A QFD team should have up to a dozen members with representation from all sections concerned with the development and launch of the product. Team composition may vary depending on whether new products or the improvement of existing products is under consideration. The important thing is that there is representation from all relevant sections and disciplines. There may well be a case for bringing in outsiders to stimulate the creative process and to ask the "silly" questions. Team members must have the support of their section heads. These section heads may feel it necessary to form a steering group. QFD teams are not usually full time, but must be given sufficient time priority to avoid time clashes. The team leader may be full time for an important QFD. The essential characteristics are team leadership skills rather than a particular branch of knowledge.

Relationship with other techniques

As mentioned. QFD is a "meta" technique in that several other techniques can be fitted in with it. For example, value management may be used to explore some of the technical alternatives, costs and trade-offs in greater detail. Taguchi analysis is commonly used with QFD because it is ideally suited to examining the most sensitive engineering characteristics so as to produce a robust design. Failure mode and effect analysis (FMEA) can be used to examine consequences of failure, and so to throw more light on the technical interactions matrix. And mention has already been made of the use of various "New Tools". In the way the QFD team carries out its work, weights alternatives, generates alternatives, groups characteristics, and so on, there are many possibilities. QFD only provides the broad concept. There is much opportunity for adaptation and innovation.

Further reading:

Ronald G. Day, *Quality Function Deployment*, ASQC Quality Press, Milwaukee, WI, 1994
Lou Cohen, *Quality Function Deployment : How to make QFD work for you*, Addison Wesley, Reading MA, 1995

Web sites

http://www.nauticom.net/www/qfdi/
http://mijuno.larc.nasa.gov/dfc/qfd.html
Lou Cohen site : http://www.awl.com/cp/cohen.html

Relationships and Encounters

In Customer Service, it has been suggested by Gutek, there are two broad types of customer interaction, "relationships" and "encounters". A pure encounter is where the customer and service provider never expect to meet again. Buying an ice cream from a street vendor is an example. A pure relationship is built over the long term, where there are frequent interactions, and where each party learns more about the other's circumstances, needs and expectations. An example would be a long established relationship between a doctor and a patient suffering from a debilitating illness.

Encounters are generally better for speed (in the short term), efficiency, and uniformity. Higher volumes are possible, and costs come down. The "production line approach to service", described by Levitt, of MacDonald's where all stages are pre-designed, standardised, and failsafed for consistency and efficiency, is a supreme example. A relationship is more labour intensive, requiring commitment and energy expenditure on both sides. But, over the longer term, relationships can become efficient (since needs and expectations are already known), tailor-made, and profitable (see the section on Zero Defections). As a result, many service providers are trying to make encounters more relationship-like or creating "pseudo relationships" (for instance, building a file on the likes and dislikes of regular hotel guests or supermarket customers). But there may also be opportunities to make traditional relationships more encounter-like, for instance "legal shops" found in the USA, production-line eye-surgery in Russia, or streamlined spectacle service.

The distinction between encounters and relationships is useful for service delivery design. One can think of a spectrum from pure encounter at one extreme to pure relationship at the other. Then it is a strategic decision where to place your business along the spectrum. In positioning a university, for example, the Senate should decide where along the spectrum from encounters to relationships it wishes to be in its dealing with students. On the one hand , students could be taught sausage machine-style by outside lecturers in large groups at low cost (allowing professors to get on with building their research reputation ?), or at the other extreme professors could teach students in small groups at much higher cost (and having much more limited research time). Both may be viable positions, but the choice should not be left to chance. It also "takes two to tango"; a customer might not want a "relationship".

On either side of the main encounter-relationship axis is the question of information intensity. One can build a low information relationship (as with a hairdresser or taxi driver), or a high-information encounter (as with selling unit trusts or insurance by mail order). Virtually every service business in the world can benefit from asking where it now sits on the matrix, and where the most appropriate place for it to sit should be.

The concept of relationships and encounters is closely associated with the issue of customer retention. See the separate section.

Further reading:
Barbara Gutek, *The Dynamics of Service*, Jossey Bass, San Francisco, 1995

Service Blueprinting

Service blueprinting is the procedure of making a flowchart or map of a service process. This is one the longest established service mapping tools and was originally proposed by Shoestack. This technique has much in common with industrial engineering flowcharting, except that customer links are specifically included. The aim is to identify points at which the service may fail to satisfy customers and to identify points where value may be added for customers. A service blueprint shows time horizontally, and the hierarchy of support vertically. In drawing up a blueprint, four areas are included :

* "customer actions" are the activities or interactions undertaken by the customer. These activities come into contact with two types of employee actions:
* "on stage" employee actions are visible to the customer and are separated in a service blueprint by a "line of interaction", drawn horizontally. Any vertical line crossing this line of interaction represents a direct contact or encounter between customer and front line employee.
* "backstage" employee actions are not visible to customers but are nevertheless in direct contact with customers (say by post or phone). These are separated from on stage activities by a "line of visibility", thus making clear what customers can see and possibly be influenced by.
* "support processes" are all those activities that support the frontline staff, whether visible or not. These are separated from backstage activities by a "line of internal interaction". Vertical lines crossing the line of internal interaction represent internal encounters.

TECHNIQUES

A service blueprint can be read horizontally to focus on customer support activities and to answer questions such as how efficient, and how many points of contact are involved. Alternatively, a blueprint can be used to gain an overview or to understand the depth and nature of the support infrastructure, in which case it is read vertically. An immediate impression of the complexity of the service process is given by a blueprint, as are the steps that a customer faces in dealing with an organisation. An illustration is shown in the figure.

The power of service blueprints can be added to by including "pre", and "post" activities, pokayoke, and the Kano model. (See the section on Cycle of Service and Customer processing.) A service blueprint can be a particularly good device for training or standardisation purposes, where photos can be added. Service can be standardised by maintaining the up-to-date position on a computer service blueprint, possibly supported by digital photo or even video.

SERVICE BLUEPRINTING
Student Registration Example

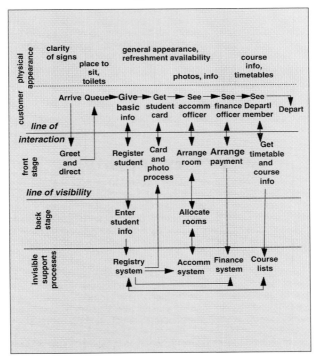

Further, service blueprinting can be the basis of "service positioning" using the SERVQUAL dimensions (see separate section) of "RATER". Thus a service interaction can be designed using a blueprint to specifically emphasise Reliability (say by providing computer-based maintenance backup), Assurance (say by emphasising care and security), Tangibles (giving particular emphasis to on stage activities and visibles), Empathy (say by emphasising individual care), and Responsiveness (say by providing extra capacity to enable staff to be flexible).

Further reading :
G. Lynn Shoestack, "Designing Services that Deliver", *Harvard Business Review*, Jan / Feb 1984, pp 133-139
G. Lynn Shoestack, "Service Positioning Through Structural Change", *Journal of Marketing*, Vol 51, January 1987, pp 34-43
Jane Kingman Brundage, "Service Mapping : Gaining a Concrete Perspective on Service System Design", in Eberhard Scheuing and William Christopher (eds), *The Service Quality Handbook*, Amacom, New York, 1993, pages 148-163

Service Gaps, "SERVQUAL" and Service Dimensions

Zeithaml, Parasuraman and Berry (or PZB are they are sometimes known) have, over several years, developed a well researched and tested methodology for identifying the dimensions of service quality and the causes of "gaps" that exist between the service that customers expect and the perceived service that is received. The methodology is presented in detail in their book, which includes questionnaires that can often be used directly with customers. These have been widely used in service industry.

The author's set of five "dimensions of service quality" can be compared with David Garvin's dimensions - see under "The Gurus". Customers in service make up their mind about the quality of service by considering each of these five, although an individual customer would have his or her own preferences or weightings between them. The five are (1) "Tangibles", which includes the physical appearance of people equipment and facilities (2) "Reliability", which is to do with ability to perform the service dependably and accurately (i.e. doing what they say they will do, on time and to specification), (3) "Responsiveness", which concerns willingness to help and to respond to individual requirements, (4) "Assurance", which is the possession of the required knowledge, the skill to perform the service, and to convey trust, confidence, and security (5) "Empathy" which begins with an understanding of the customer's needs and the ability to provide an individualised service. (These can be remembered by the mnemonic RATER). Taken together the five are known as "SERVQUAL", a registered phrase which is widely known. Like Garvin's dimensions, these are a very useful checklist. The authors have found, in a wide variety of surveys in different service sectors, where customers are asked to allocate 100 points between the five factors to indicate relative importance, that the Reliability dimension is the one which is most highly valued. The next two highest valued dimensions are Responsiveness and Assurance.

SERVQUAL helps identify customer perceptions of service quality. The 'gaps' analysis takes this further and helps identify the causes of service quality shortfalls in each or all of the dimensions. According to the authors, customers build an expectation of the service to be received depending on four factors. These are, firstly, word-of-mouth communications obtained from friends and acquaintances, secondly, personal needs, thirdly, past experience plays a part and, lastly, communications put out by the service company create their own expectations. The authors refer to "Gap 5" as being the difference between expected service and the perceived service experienced. Gap 5 results from a combination of Gaps 1 to 4. These are :

Gap 1 results from a difference between what customers expect and what management perceives these expectations to be. This can occur, for example, as a result of management not undertaking sufficient research or from communication failures within the company

T
E
C
H
N
I
Q
U
E
S

Gap 2 results from a difference between management perceptions of what customers expect and the specifications that management draws up, or fails to draw up, spelling out what service quality delivery actions are required. This can result from inadequate management commitment and interest, from a perception that the company cannot actually meet customer requirements, from a failure to specify in detail what is required, or from a failure in the way in which the company sets its goals in relation to customers.

The "PZB" SERVICE GAPS

lack of market research, inadequate upward communication — **Gap 1**

Customer's Expected Service

inadequate management commitment, perceived as infeasible, etc — **Gap 2**

Management Perceptions of Customer Expectations

role conflict, poor employee job fit, inappropriate controls, lack of teamwork, etc — **Gap 3**

Management Specifications for Service Delivery

Gap 5

Actual Service Delivery

inadequate horiz communication, "propensity to overpromise" etc — **Gap 4**

Perceived Service Delivery

Communications about Service Delivery

adapted from
Ziethami, Parasuraman, and Berry
"Delivering Service Quality", Free Press, 1990

Gap 3 results from a mismatch between the service delivery specifications required by management and the actual service that is delivered by front line staff. There are many possible causes of this gap. Some include inappropriate technology, inappropriate staff or training, poor teamwork, and inappropriate control measures and methods.

Finally Gap 4 results from a difference between the actual service that is delivered and messages that are put out to customers about what to expect. Clearly a major reason for this is poor internal communication and lack of familiarity with operations. There is also the often-found "propensity to overpromise". Clearly it is more desirable to under-promise and over-deliver.

The fact that, under SERVQUAL, service quality is determined by the overall gap between what was expected and what was delivered, is of importance. It means that service quality is relative not absolute, and that different customers may perceive the level of service quality differently; that quality is determined by the customer who has "all the votes", not by the service provider; that service quality can be achieved by either meeting or exceeding expectations (see the Kano model), or by changing expectations (Gap 4, above).

Recent work has shown that the SERVQUAL dimensions and weightings do not necessarily apply in all parts of the world. For instance, Far East airline passengers seem to value respect above reliability.

Sweden's Christian Grönroos views service quality as having 6 dimensions, the first four of which are roughly in line with those of PZB. These are Professionalism and Skills (assurance), Attitudes and Behaviour (empathy), Accessibility and Flexibility (responsiveness), and Reliability and Trustworthiness (reliability). Grönroos' additional two factors are Recovery and Problem Solving (the importance of which has been stressed by Reichheld and Sasser in their work on customer retention (see separate section), and Reputation and Credibility (to do with the image of the business in the mind of the customer, which overlaps with the concept of capability by Heskett, Sasser and Schlesinger (see the section on The Service Profit Chain).

Further reading
Valerie Zeithaml, A. Parasuraman, and Leonard Berry, *Delivering Quality Service*, Free Press, New York,1990.
Dick Schaaf, *Keeping the Edge : Giving Customers the Service they Demand*, Plume Penguin, New York, 1997, Part 2.

The Service Profit Chain

The Service Profit Chain is a series of concepts developed by Heskett, Sasser and Schlesinger following years of research at Harvard Business School. It builds on work on customer loyalty and retention (see separate section). To quote the authors : "Service profit chain thinking maintains that there are direct and strong relationships between profit; growth; customer loyalty; customer satisfaction; the value of goods and services delivered to customers; and employee capability, satisfaction, loyalty, and productivity". The book on the topic is a "tour de force" on service quality, with much relevance for manufacturing also.

A central feature of the service profit chain is an equation for customer value which is

Customer Value =   Results + Process Quality
                     Price + Customer Access Costs

The **"results"** obtained by a targeted customer are the benefits derived. This is similar to the established marketing idea that customers actually purchase outcomes or benefits, rather than products or services. **Process quality** covers the elements of service quality such as the RATER (Reliability, Assurance, Tangibles, Empathy, Responsiveness) proposed by Parasuraman, Zeithaml and Berry in their SERVQUAL work (see separate section). **Price,** of course, affects expectations. Finally, **access costs** are to do with convenience in time and place of acquiring the service.

T
E
C
H
N
I
Q
U
E
S

The service profit chain establishes a feedback loop from employees, to service delivery, to customer satisfaction, to customer retention and loyalty, resulting in improved growth and profitability which in turn affects employee satisfaction and the ability to provide better information, workplaces, and other facilities and tools. Within the overall chain there are many linkages which affect one another.

The Service Profit Chain

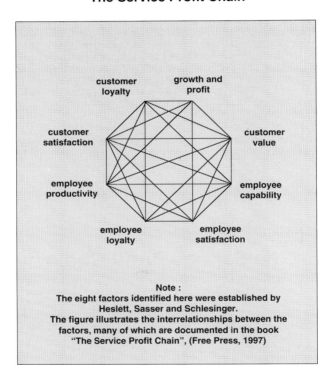

customer loyalty

growth and profit

customer satisfaction

customer value

employee productivity

employee capability

employee loyalty

employee satisfaction

Note :
The eight factors identified here were established by Heslett, Sasser and Schlesinger. The figure illustrates the interrelationships between the factors, many of which are documented in the book "The Service Profit Chain", (Free Press, 1997)

On the customer side, the authors have identified and established links between the elements of the profit chain, as shown in the figure. Many of the linkages shown have been researched amongst leading companies, but much remains to be done. The service profit chain therefore provides a useful and interesting framework both for managers and for academic research. As such it is a very comprehensive work, the relevance of which can only grow.

Further reading
James Heskett, W Earl Sasser, Leonard Schlesinger, *The Service Profit Chain*, The Free Press, New York, 1997

Service Recovery, Customer Retention and the "Three R's"

Two significant pieces of research are highlighted in this section which, when combined, have great significance for customer retention in service business.

The first is a study by Reichheld and Sasser. These researchers reported the powerful impact of customer defections on the "bottom line". Several cases are quoted. (For example in a credit card company, priority was given to gathering information from defecting customers, adjusting products and services accordingly. As a result profits increased sixteen fold without acquisitions). Retained customers generate increasing profits the longer they stay : setup costs are paid, advertising costs decline, and prices may be increased. One rule of thumb is that it costs 5 times as much to acquire a new customer as it does to retain an existing one. As a result, Reichheld and Sasser maintain that customer retention is a more important determinant of profitability than market share.

The second is work by Technical Assistance Research Programs, Inc. a U.S. based research organisation which has produced some widely quoted, and very significant , findings which are especially important to service quality in general and "service recovery" (i.e. recovering from poor service delivery) in particular.

In response to the Question "How many of your unhappy customers will buy other products or services offered by your company?", TARP found that, for small and medium purchases:

* approximately 85% of customers who had experienced no problem would repurchase.
* only around 45% of customers who are dissatisfied and who complain, would repurchase.
* but, where the complaint is "mollified" the repurchase percentage rises to around 80%,
* and, where the complainant is satisfied, the percentage exceeds 90% (i.e. above the percentage who experienced no problem!).

TARP also found (U.S. figures) that only a small percentage of dissatisfied customers (perhaps 20%) actually complain, but even less (perhaps 4%) go to the trouble to write. The point is that many front line complaints are lost though employees not passing on the information. Worse though is the finding that dissatisfied customers do not complain to the company, but nevertheless tell an average of 9 to 10 other people. TARP also found that approximately one third of complaints relate to problems caused by customers themselves (for example, unclear instructions).

Customer retention should therefore be a high priority. Ways to go about this include the following:

* "Watching the Door", or identifying customers who have just "defected" or who are about to leave. Sometimes this can be easy where there are established accounts which have become non-operative (or even where use has declined significantly), but may be more difficult where customers are nameless as in retailing. Here loyalty schemes such as store cards may be an answer. An efficient feedback process as to the reasons for defections is required. Of course, it should be kept up to date.
* Making complaining easier. Passive customer survey information collection is routinely attempted at hotels, but ways need to be found to make this more active by, for example, rewards. In any case have free phone or reply paid mail.
* A "no quibble" policy on returns.
* Key account management, including careful and regular monitoring.
* Trying to stay ahead of the game by identifying future expectations. One way is to work through so called "lead users" - the innovators who buy early.
* Eliminating any "climate of fear" as Deming would have called it, which prevents onward communication of poor performance. An attitude that a dissatisfied customer is an opportunity not a threat needs to pervade an organisation, but is especially important for first tier managers.

* Offer some compensation, even if small : a voucher or free meal. In Britain "service guarantees" are offered by telephone and water companies.
* Have a preplanned service recovery process : recognise that some service failures are predicable, others not, but that a routine should be worked out for the former category. This routine swings into place automatically when service failure occurs. Of course, such routines should not prevent seeking a failsafe solution.
* Explain what happened to the customer. TARP research suggests that a clear explanation is more effective than just fixing the problem.
* Giving employees the authority to solve customer problems right there and then; don't add to the problem by shifting responsibility.

Heskett, Sasser and Schlesinger have therefore proposed an extension to the traditional 4 P's of marketing (Product, Price, Place, Promotion), as being more appropriate to the service firm (but, no doubt, also very relevant to manufacturing firms that invariably bundle product and service). These are the Three R's : Retention, Referrals, and Related Products. Retention is the ability to hold on to valuable customers (whilst also identifying and dropping low loyalty, very dissatisfied customers - whom these authors refer to as "terrorists"). Referrals is the ability to gain from word of mouth recommendations - which are not only free but the have the highest credibility. And selling related products and services is made easier and more cost effective by the reputation for value and customer care from loyal customers.

Further readings:
Frederick Reichheld and W Earl Sasser Jr., "Zero Defections : Quality Comes to Services", *Harvard Business Review*, Vol 70, Sept./ October 1990, pages 105-111.
Frederick Reichheld, *The Loyalty Effect*, Harvard Business School Press, Boston, 1996.
Technical Assistance Research Programs, *Consumer Complaint Handling in America : an Update Study*, U.S. Office of Consumer Affairs, March 1986.
Valerie Zeithaml and Mary Jo Bitner, *Services Marketing*, Mc Graw Hill, New York, 1996, Chapters 6 and 16.
James Heskett, W Earl Sasser, Leonard Schlesinger, *The Service Profit Chain*, The Free Press, New York, 1997

Six Sigma

TECHNIQUES

"Six Sigma" is concept and aim developed by the Motorola company but now adopted by many others. Motorola defined Six Sigma as "a measure of goodness - the capability of a process to produce perfect work". The Six Sigma concept is about the aim of making all processes in the chain highly capable; that is achieving a capability index of at least two. Six Sigma refers to the number of standard deviations from the average setting of a process to the tolerance limit. In statistical terms, this translates to 3.4 defects per million opportunities for error. At Motorola this concept has been extended to every function in the company, where everyone is considered to be both a supplier and a customer. For such levels of quality, both design and manufacturing must play a role.

"Sigma" refers to the symbol that is used for the standard deviation of the normal distribution (∂). In statistical process control, when samples are taken from a process the readings are expected to stay within plus or minus three standard deviations of the mean. If a sample is taken which plots outside of these limits the process is said to be "out of control". It should then be stopped and investigated. There is still a small chance that an in-control reading will be taken outside of these limits. If however the tolerance limits are located at plus or minus six sigma, then it is highly likely that a deviating process will be stopped well before defects are made. So six sigma refers to the aim of reducing process variance to half the distance between specification limits. This gives a capability index of two. Refer to the section on SPC for the exact formulas.

When Motorola announced its Six Sigma programme, such levels of process capability were rare. Most product manufacturing chains were found to have quality levels at five or even four sigma (which is still a good standard not achieved today by many companies). Expressing the company goal as six sigma made for a clear aim. It also acts as a guide to priorities, because those processes with the lowest sigma ratings could be targeted first and all new products (for example Motorola's Keynote pager) would have six sigma as the target quality level.

SIX SIGMA

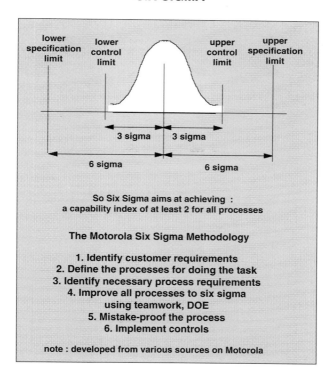

So Six Sigma aims at achieving :
a capability index of at least 2 for all processes

The Motorola Six Sigma Methodology

1. Identify customer requirements
2. Define the processes for doing the task
3. Identify necessary process requirements
4. Improve all processes to six sigma
using teamwork, DOE
5. Mistake-proof the process
6. Implement controls

note : developed from various sources on Motorola

Motorola has attacked the Six Sigma objective through a variety of means, but team involvement and design of experiments have been particularly important.

Sixth Sigma

"Sigma" is the standard term for one standard deviation in the normal distribution. The sixth sigma approach is named after the spread of the normal distribution, which for all practical purposes extends for three standard deviations on each side of the average value, that is over six sigma. As with SPC, points that lie within the six sigma spread indicate "common cause" or "normal" events, but points outside represent "special" events which call for investigation. Sixth sigma concentrates attention on the best normal events.

The **Sixth sigma** approach is particularly applicable in non-manufacturing activities. Here the interest concentrates on the topmost standard deviation. This is where the best performance is to be found, and as with Pareto analysis it is where the greatest benefit can be gained. (In some cases it is the first sigma; but for illustration we will assume the sixth.) Statistically the sixth sigma contains only about 2.3% of the total events, but you may wish to think in terms of the top 5%. Having researched and distilled what it is that allows this top performance, the task is then to transfer this knowledge or method to all relevant people.

SIXTH SIGMA

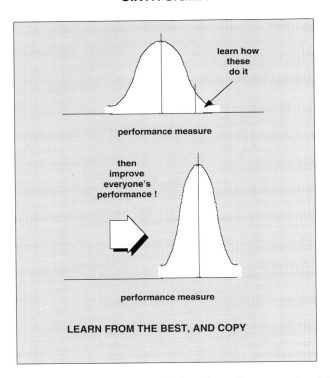

learn how these do it

performance measure

then improve everyone's performance !

performance measure

LEARN FROM THE BEST, AND COPY

An example aids clarity: Let us say you are monitoring sales performance using sixth sigma. The best sales performances are to be found in the sixth sigma region. Now you would be interested in whether this superior performance is achieved by relatively few salespersons. (The method can be used in conjunction with the technique of stratification -see the 7 tools.) If so, what is it that gives them this edge? What is it that they do that is different from what others do? Find it out by careful study and systematic comparison between the super- and the ordinary-performers. (Is it the way they greet their client? Is it the preparation? Is it to do with follow-up?). Eventually you determine the points of difference. Now "let everyone in on the secret".

The sixth sigma approach goes beyond training in the standard methods. The standard method produces a natural variation in performance. But some will adapt the standard method with their own innovations that will occasionally result in truly outstanding performance. They may not know what it is that they do or say that causes "breakthrough", as Juran would call it.

Supplier Partnerships

The concept of supplier partners developed strongly in the 1980's as a result of the movement towards just-in-time (JIT) manufacturing. JIT emphasises reduction in waste, shortening of lead times, improvement in quality, continuous improvement, and simplicity. These are the goals of supplier partnership, also. Today supplier partnerships are found both in service and manufacturing.

The philosophy is that, through cooperation rather than confrontation, both parties benefit. It is a longer term view, emphasising total cost rather than product price. Cost includes not only today's price of the part or product, but also its quality (defect / ppm rate), delivery reliability, delivery frequency, the simplicity with which the transaction is processed, and the future potential for price reductions.

But partnership goes further : Long term, stable relationships are sought rather than short term, adversarial, quick advantage transactions. The analogy of a marriage is often used. It may have its ups and downs, but commitment remains. In a partnership, contracts will be longer term to give the supplier confidence and the motivation to invest and improve. Both parties recognise that the game whereby low prices are bid and then argued up on contingencies once the contract is awarded, is wasteful and counterproductive. Instead, it may be possible for both parties to cooperate on price reduction, sharing the benefits between them. Such cooperation may be achieved through the temporary secondment of staff.

For partnership to work, there must of necessity be few or single suppliers per part. There is not necessarily a risk of "being taken for a ride" because there is too much for a supplier to loose, and much to gain (such as reductions in bidding costs). There may however be a risk of disruption in supply. This should be a calculated risk; where the probability is very small the advantages of a single supplier may outweigh the risks. And there are ways around this too : having one supplier exclusively supplying a part to one plant, but another supplier exclusively supplying the same part to another plant. This spreads the risk whilst still achieving single supplier advantages. Alternatively there is the Japanese practice of cultivating several suppliers simultaneously but then awarding an exclusive contract to one supplier of a part for the life of the product, and selecting another supplier for a similar part going into another end product. The idea is to work with a few good, trusted suppliers who supply a wide range of parts. Partnership has therefore resulted in drastic reductions in many a company's supplier base. An objective is to remove the long tail of the supplier Pareto curve whereby perhaps 10% of parts are supplied by 80% of the suppliers.

Usually, partnership begins with a Pareto-type analysis of suppliers by cost and number of parts. Often it will be found that a large number of suppliers supply a very small proportion of value. Then, exploration as to how to reduce or combine sourcing begins. Award business to those identified as potential partners, and gradually drop the rest. Supplier days are held, often annually, when company plans and objectives are explained, measures given, prizes for best performance given out, and factory tours held. For true partnership, director level meetings are held periodically, with much more frequent manager and engineer contact.

On quality, a partnership aims at zero receiving inspection and delivery directly to the point of use. (By the way, partnership quality should talk in terms of ppm levels, not percentages.) Packaging and part orientation may be specifically designed to reduce waste. Delivery would often be subject to kanban call-off : the partner would be given long term forecasts of gross requirements far out, more detailed requirements close in, but the actual sequence and timing of delivery is controlled by kanban. Many attempt this, far fewer achieve it. Both sides need to work towards schedule stability : the customer to not change his mind at the last moment, and the supplier to provide reliable delivery. The point is, there should be advantages for both sides : unstable schedules ultimately cost the customer in terms of money and risk, and reduce the possibility of productivity gain at the supplier.

Sometimes, the supplier is responsible for maintaining inventory levels at a customer, called VMI (vendor managed inventory) which is increasingly found for consumables. Other times, a manufacturer may write the production schedule of the supplier. As trust builds, self billing or reconciliation becomes possible ("we built 100 cars, so here is our cheque for the 500 tyres we must have used"). An advanced form is "JITII" (a registered mark of the Bose corporation) whereby a few major suppliers have full time representatives in the host plant, with access to company records and schedules, and whose responsibilities include writing purchase orders on their own company. Such reps also participate in design work and R&D, and attend company planning meetings. JITII is now beginning to be found outside of Bose in companies such as Hewlett Packard and Intel. These partnership arrangements stem from the interesting insight of Lance Dixon that it is actually more secure to have a supplier write purchase orders on himself than it is for one of your own staff to do so (because legal action can recover damages from a supplier resulting from negligence, but seldom can be recovered from your own employee!).

Improved communication links via EDI or EPOS further enhance partnership advantages. Delivery cooperation becomes possible either through "milkrounds" (whereby small quantities are collected from several firms in an area every day, rather than from one firm once per week), or , where more work is given to one supplier, mixed loads are sent every day rather than one-product loads once per week. This improves flow and reduces inventories.

Cooperation on design is part of partnership. The manufacturer recognises the supplier's ability to design the parts that it makes, rather than simply specifying. This policy of "open specs" or "black box" specs can lead to faster product development, lower cost, and more up to date part supply. The partnership idea encourages the concept of a company sticking to its core business, whilst putting out non-core business.

Generally, supplier partnership makes sense for "A" and possibly "B" parts; less so for commodity items. Part criticality and risk also influence the partnership decision; you would not risk partnership with a company having poor industrial relations, or weak finances, or poor quality assurance. This means that a team approach is necessary in supplier selection. The Purchasing Officer may coordinate, but throughout the partnership Design would talk to their opposite number in Design, Quality to Quality, Production control to Production control, and so on.

Disadvantages ? Time, commitment, costs of establishment, risk of inappropriate choices of partner, and short term cost reduction opportunities foregone against medium term gains.

Value engineering is a technique that both parties may adopt for mutual advantage. VE/VA is a powerful technique for cost, quality and delivery. In advanced partnerships a "satellite plant" dedicated to a particular customer and located nearby, or "suppliers in residence" where the supplier's operation and or some of its staff are permanently located on the customer's site, may be worth consideration. Volkswagen's Brazilian plants are reported to use supplier's employees on the VW assembly line - is this the future of partnership, or a quest for flexibility?

In Japan, and increasingly in the rest of the world, supplier partnership is now expanding down from relationships with first tier suppliers, to second and even third tier. Larger firms in the car industry have been leaders, but other industries and smaller firms are following. The thought, in common with TQM, is that quality is only as good as the weakest link in the supply chain or network.

Further reading:
James Womack, Daniel Jones, Daniel Roos, *The Machine that Changed the World,* Rawson Associates, New York, 1990, Chapter 6.
Richard Schonberger and Edward Knod, *Operations Management*, Irwin, Illinois, 1994, Chapter 8
Peter Hines, *Creating World Class Suppliers : Unlocking mutual competitive advantage*, Pitman, London, 1994,
Richard Lamming, *Beyond Partnership*, Prentice Hall, Hemel Hempstead, 1993,
Lance Dixon and Anne Millen Porter, *JITII : Revolution in Buying and Selling*, Purchasing Magazine / Cahners, Newton, MA, 1994

Yield Management

There are two meanings for "yield management. In the **Quality context,** "yield" refers to the ratio of output to input. This is important for some industries such as microprocessors and chemicals. Sometimes yield ratios get built into MRP systems which then automatically generate the extra requirements necessary to produce a required output. As Juran has pointed out, there is a danger in this in as far as this underlying or "chronic" waste comes to be seen as the norm, about which nothing is done. So "yield" needs to be recognised and tackled. Good tools are Taguchi methods and the seven tools of quality.

In the **Service context,** yield management is about capacity allocation at the right price and the right time so as to yield maximum profit. The origins are in the airline industry where, as everyone has experienced perhaps with some frustration, a whole range of seat prices are in operation on any one flight.

So why is yield management an important issue? Simply this : it is about making the best use of available capacity, whether in transport, hotels, fitness clubs, restaurants, conferences, or whatever. And now we are beginning to see yield management applied outside of services in manufacturing such as own-brand foods, and car spare parts. In fact, yield management is applicable wherever there is unused fixed capacity, high fixed costs, low variable costs, and similarity of units. These are exactly the characteristics that one finds with airline seats. Yield management has been around for a long time, but formal computer-based models only emerged in the mid 1980's

Requirements for establishing a yield management system include : Market Segmentation whereby customers are identified and segmented by willingness to accept different terms and conditions. Pricing analysis follows this. Of course, lower prices are offered at less favourable times, and competitor prices must be tracked. Forecasts must be made of the demand by segment. Booking curves which show the build-up of bookings over time before the delivery date are required. Lastly, many yield systems incorporate an overbooking policy to allow for "no-shows". No show data should be available, as well as the policy and compensation for overcapacity situations. And, of course, all these requirements should be held together and updated in an information system. A good information system should be able to track and forecast seasonal or even daily variations - for example, the number of "no shows" on a Friday is 10% but on other days it is 6%.

Yield is defined as : (revenue realised) x 100 / revenue potential. A basic principle is to continue to offer discounted capacity until the risk of losing the net contribution from full price payers becomes unacceptably high. With words like "risk" and "unacceptably" one appreciates that yield management is a matter of probability and judgment. But simple systems can be very effective provided they assemble and use information effectively. In a hotel, for example, with a good information system, it may be good enough to calculate on a daily basis the number of rooms to be allowed for by a rolling forecast of rooms booked less departures plus scheduled arrivals plus walk-ins minus no-shows. The result is either a quantity of overbookings to be allowed for or a quantity of shortfall which can be offered to (say) a tour operator having compatible clientele. This rolling process is undertaken based on booking levels made (say) two months in advance, and the information system should be capable of predicting changes in all variables depending on the season.

At the other extreme, there are several quantitative approaches available for yield management,

**T
E
C
H
N
I
Q
U
E
S**

from economic models to mathematical programming. As an example, the linear programming formulation is as follows :

Maximise
$$\sum_i r_i x_i$$

subject to
$$\sum_i x_i \le C$$
$$x_i \le D_i$$
$$x_i, D_i \ge 0$$

where
r is the revenue per unit of type i
x is the number of units of type i to be offered
C is the total available capacity in units
D is the demand for units of type i

Models, both mathematical programming and economic analysis based, get much more complex than this, and today airlines and hotel chains are major users.

Finally, if overbooking is a possibility, yield management requires careful consideration of legal matters. There may be claims for compensation, breach of contract or deceptive trade practices. Staff handling orders or customers must then be trained on what to say and do. Seek legal advice.

Further reading :
Ian Yeoman and Anthony Ingold (eds), *Yield Management*, Cassell, London, 1997.

T
E
C
H
N
I
Q
U
E
S

TECHNIQUES

The Systems

ISO 9000
The Baldridge and
EFQM Award

ISO 9000 Series, QS-9000

The International Standard BS EN ISO 9000 (previously known as British Standard 5750) is the world standard code of practice for Quality Assurance systems. Assurance is "those planned and systematic actions necessary to provide adequate confidence that a product or service will satisfy given requirements for quality." Two common misconceptions must be cleared up immediately: These are, firstly, the standards are not about actual product or service quality. It is quite possible to be registered under ISO 9000 and still be producing products which are defective and not to customer requirements. (As the CEO of Motorola has observed, "it is quite possible to make life jackets out of concrete and still be registered.") Product quality is not necessarily better than that in non registered companies. The second misconception is that the standards lay down a set of procedures to be followed; they do not and could not for every company. To some, especially smaller companies, ISO 9000 is unnecessary bureaucracy. John Seddon has argued that ISO 9000 has often turned out to be an inflexible set of rules, to the detriment of continuous improvement. The ISO Technical Committee on the other hand argues that ISO 9000 is the basis for continuous improvement. But to many it is a way of demonstrating, internationally, that the company takes quality seriously and has thought through its quality system. It has become a marketing advantage and a trade facilitator. By 1997 over 100,000 certificates had been awarded worldwide with around half in the UK.

What the standards do is to require conformity to documented practices specified in the company's own quality systems. The standards give the areas that need to be considered; the company installs its own most suitable response; documents it, maintains it, updates it, and guarantees that its own procedures are followed. Unannounced external audits are necessary to ensure compliance of the company with its own standards. In other words ISO 9000 is really about "saying what you do, and doing what you say". Certification can only be awarded by an accredited third-party registrar. Certification would involve a company in (at least) preparing a written policy statement, writing a quality manual on its own systems and procedures, as well as making available all documents and controls as required.

One might argue that the 19 clauses of ISO 9000 make perfect common sense for every business, and simply require the documentation of steps that should be done anyway : (1) management must accept responsibility (2) a quality system must be set up (3) contracts must be reviewed (4) designs require control (5) requires document control (6) and (7) deal with purchasing (8) covers product identification and traceability (9) process control (10) inspection and testing (11) test equipment (12) inspection status (13) control of nonconforming product (14) corrective action (15) handling, storage and packaging (16) quality records (17) internal quality audits (18) servicing and (19) statistical control.

ISO 9000-1 gives Quality management and quality assurance standards: Guidelines for selection and use. This is the document to use when deciding which is the applicable standard (i.e. 9001 to 9003) and how it is to be used. The document is "suitable for the purpose of (a company) demonstrating its capability and for assessment of (those) capabilities by external parties". It is "aimed primarily at achieving customer satisfaction by preventing nonconformance at all stages from design to servicing". Buried away in 9000-1 is reference to a "main document" which is the central Quality Manual, essential to registration. A Quality Manual documents the entire quality system procedures to be followed and names specific individuals to be responsible for the various tasks.

ISO9004-1, strangely, follows on from 9000-1 and is the most comprehensive guide to the standards. It deals with "Quality management and quality system elements : Guidelines" and covers Policy and objectives, Organisation and responsibility, Marketing, Design, Procurement, Production, Equipment control, Documentation, and Verification. Special emphasis is placed on "quality awareness", the implication being that everyone's contributes to customer satisfaction. Part 2 deals with services. There are two headings under which services can be measured either quantitatively or qualitatively. "Service requirements" are directly observable by the customer,

**S
Y
S
T
E
M
S**

whilst "Service delivery requirements" may not always be observable but will affect the service provided. The latest revision of ISO 9000 introduced the term "stakeholder" to emphasize that employees, owners, sub-suppliers, and society (as well as customers) should benefit.

The standards are arranged in a hierarchical way with 9003 included in 9002 which is in turn included in 9001. ISO 9001 concerns Quality Systems in design, development, production, installation, and servicing. This is the full standard applicable when design and development is to be assured as well as producing and distributing. This is for the most complex case, and contains 20 elements. One important aspect is that of contract review which covers documentation of contracts and the supplier's ability to meet the contractual requirements. 9002 is the more common, cut down version of 9001 to be used for assurance when there is an existing design or specification. 9003 is the least complex standard applicable when conformance is to be assured solely on the basis of inspection and testing.

In addition to the 9000 series, ISO 8402 deals with the vocabulary used in the standards. It is presented in three languages. Interestingly, the standard recognises that other sources define quality as "fitness for purpose" and "conformance to specification", but then makes the point that a more full explanation is required.

QS-9000 is the car industry version of ISO 9000. It contains ISO 9001 but its requirements are much broader than ISO 9001. It was developed because it was felt that ISO 9000 was not current for the car industry. By the end of 1997, Ford, Chrysler and GM require all current suppliers to have achieved third-party recognition.

Further reading
Kit Sadgrove, *ISO9000/ BS5750 Made Easy*, Kogan Page, London, 1994
Greg Hutchins, *ISO9000*, (Second edition), Wiley, New York, 1997
John Seddon, *In Pursuit of Quality : The Case Against ISO 9000*, Oak Tree Press, 1997

Web Sites
The following site gives up to date news on ISO 9000 developments
http://www.iso.ch/9000e/news.html
The US government version, containing search possibilities
http:/www.mep.nist.gov/resources/iso9000/iso9000.html
A site which has had an "open forum" on the use of ISO 9000 in small business is
http://www.salford.ac.uk/man~sch/iso.html
The ISO site is at http://www.iso.ch

The BALDRIDGE AWARD
and EFQM AWARD.

The Malcolm Baldridge National Quality Award was established as a U.S. Public Law in 1987 and is administered by the U.S. National Institute of Standards and Technologies (NIST). The aims of the "Baldridge" are
* to stimulate companies to improve quality
* to recognise achievement in quality
* to establish guidelines for self evaluation
* to publicise successes in quality and learn from the winners

The real purpose of the Baldridge is to educate. It should not be seen as an alternative to ISO 9000 which does not address many categories covered by Baldridge. They should be regarded as complimentary. Self assessment is at the heart of the Baldridge and EFQM awards, and the ease with which this can be done is perhaps their greatest attraction.

Although the Baldridge is a competition for U.S. companies it has become perhaps the most comprehensive statement on just what Total Quality really means and requires. As such the framework can be used by any company, U.S. based or not. Awards are made in three categories: manufacturing, small business, and service, and presented by the President of the United States. For U.S. companies, going in for the award is "win, win" : there is considerable prestige and market advantage in winning, or even reaching the site visit stage, but even entering forces a comprehensive discipline for the company and commitment by management.

The EFQM Excellence Model

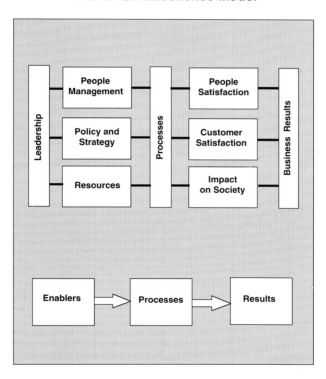

Entering requires the completion of a self assessment questionnaire and the submission of a 75 page case study. Even for non U.S. firms the guidelines are a valuable checklist. The Baldridge can be used for self evaluation, to set up Total Quality programs, for comparison purposes, and for communication guidance with suppliers and customers. The guidelines are updated annually, and available from the NIST. It is a good idea to write for the latest version.

S
Y
S
T
E
M
S

The award is structured around 4 basic elements, 7 areas, and 28 categories which should form a dynamic relationship. 1000 points are distributed. A brief summary follows:

"The Driver"

1. Senior Executive Leadership. This examines the personal commitment of senior management to quality and customer focus. Customer focus is expected to be integrated into everyday leadership, and leadership should demonstrate a concern, amongst others, for ethics and public health and safety. (3 categories, current points 95)

"The System"

2. Information and Analysis. This examines how information is used to support prevention-based quality. Information must be timely and reviewed regularly. Benchmarking must be done and kept up to date. (3 categories, current points 75)

3. Strategic Quality Planning. This examines the process of planning for, and retaining, quality leadership. Quality plans must be integrated into business plans, and measures to track performance of both the company and its suppliers kept. (2 categories, current points 75)

4. Human Resource Development and Management. This examines how the human resource is planned and managed as part of quality. How are employees involved, and how they are educated, trained, and recognised. Their morale is also considered. Performance measures must be in place, and attention given to ergonomics, health and safety. (5 categories, current points 150)

5. Management of Process Quality. This covers the processes used in design, production, support, supplier management, and quality assessment. The conversion of customer needs into products and services must be demonstrated. Prevention must be emphasised, and continuous improvement must be used. (5 categories, current points 140)

"Measures of Progress"

6. Quality and Operational Results. This examines the measurement system applied to products, services, suppliers, business processes, and operating results. Quality levels in these areas must be compared with competing companies. (4 categories, current points 180)

"The Goal"

7. Customer Focus and Satisfaction. This important area covers the company's knowledge of, interaction with, and commitment to customers. The methods used are examined, and how customers feel about the company in relation to its competitors. (6 categories, current points 300)

The scoring guidelines enable self assessment to be undertaken. They are very specific and are of two types "Approach/Deployment" and "Results". The type to be used is given for each of the 7 areas. For instance, the Results type gives 0% for no or anecdotal data, to 100% where, amongst others, "strong evidence of industry and benchmark leadership is demonstrated".

A European equivalent was started by the European Foundation for Quality Management (EFQM) in 1991. The first winner was Rank Xerox of Britain who has published its award-winning submission. The EFQM is similar in concept to the Baldridge, but has a more European "feel". It is also likely to be used by most companies as a self test of Total Quality. In fact the EFQM now emphasises that their model is one for "business excellence" (not just quality). The Enablers (or systemic factors) drive Processes which produce Results, as shown in the figure. It is a journey from cause to effect.

Most European countries now also have their own quality awards, generally based on the European model for business excellence. The UK Quality Award's recent winners include TNT Distribution and Mortgage Express.

Enablers	Points	Area
Leadership	100	the behaviour of all managers
Policy and Strategy	80	mission, values, vision, direction
People Management	90	management of company people
Resources	90	management, utilisation, preservation
Processes	140	all value adding activities
Results		
Customer Satisfaction	200	the perception of external customers
People Satisfaction	90	peoples feelings about the company
Impact on Society.	60	perception amongst the community
Business Results	150	the business performance

The awards have had their critics. Phil Crosby, for example, claimed that the Baldridge would divert attention to paperwork and procedures rather than to getting product and customer satisfaction right. Others have pointed out the low correlation between award winners and business results.

The Baldridge: Details from: NIST, Route 270 and Quince Orchard Road, Administration Building Room A537, Gaithersburg, MD 20899, U.S.A.

The EFQM : Details from; EFQM, Les Pléiades, Avenue des Pléiades 19c, 1200 Brussels, Belgium. Fax +32 2 7791237

Web sites
Full details of the EFQM from : http://www.efqm.org
The European Organisation for Quality (EOQ) is at : http://www.euroqual.org

S
Y
S
T
E
M
S

115

NOTES: